It took the human [...]
years to reach a h[...]
1800's. It became [...]
hundred years mor[...]
reproduction, we can expect an increase of
four billion in the next forty years.

SIX BILLION PEOPLE
BY THE YEAR 2008!

CAN THE EARTH
SUPPORT THEM ALL?

To bring the fullest life to the greatest number of
people we must begin to use the findings of science
today. We must use biology to improve ourselves and
our living environment. We must use chemistry to rid
the air and the water of pollutants. We must use psychology, sociology, political science and economics to
improve relationships between people and nations.
MAN IN THE WEB OF LIFE links the sciences into
a dynamic whole in a panorama of man . . . his be-
ginnings, his present state and WHERE HE CAN GO
FROM HERE.

THE AUTHOR . . . JOHN H. STORER, who gradu-
ated from Harvard in 1911, spent 24 years as a farmer,
then became a lecturer and film-maker in the cause of
conservation. His films have been translated into Spanish and Portuguese for use in South America. Mr.
Storer was president of the Florida Audobon Society
for thirteen years. His previous books are *The Flight
of Birds* and *The Web of Life*, which sold a third of
a million copies and has been translated into Spanish,
Japanese and Arabic.

Other SIGNETS You Will Enjoy Reading

John H. Storer

MAN
IN THE WEB
OF LIFE

Civilization, Science and Natural Law

A SIGNET SCIENCE LIBRARY BOOK

Published by
THE NEW AMERICAN LIBRARY,
New York and Toronto
The New English Library Limited, London

SIGNET TRADEMARK REG. U.S. PAT. OFF. AND FOREIGN COUNTRIES
REGISTERED TRADEMARK—MARCA REGISTRADA
HECHO EN CHICAGO, U.S.A.

SIGNET SCIENCE LIBRARY BOOKS are published
in the United States by The New American Library, Inc.,
1301 Avenue of the Americas, New York, New York 10019,
in Canada by The New American Library of Canada Limited,
295 King Street East, Toronto 2, Ontario,
in the United Kingdom by The New English Library Limited,
Barnard's Inn, Holborn, London, E. C. 1, England

FIRST PRINTING, NOVEMBER, 1968

PRINTED IN THE UNITED STATES OF AMERICA

preface

In the year 1910 a college student stood at the edge of a Montana wheat field. In the background lay a range of forest-covered mountains. Far down the field one of the giant new power-driven harvesting machines was gathering in the crop; this product of man's inventive genius promised a revolution in the production of food and thereby opened visions of a new life for mankind.

Suddenly around the machine there was intense activity—men running in circles, stamping down the standing grain, flailing at it with empty grain bags. A spark from the machine had caught in the tinder-dry wheat. Little wisps of smoke curled up, then flickering orange flames. Soon a long line of flame, driven by a gentle breeze, moved toward the nearby mountain. By noon, columns of smoke were drifting up from the mountain forest, and through the smoke vivid sheets of flame leaped upward.

Driven by the intense heat, tornadoes of rising air whirled great blazing branches up with them, sweeping across canyons and dropping the flames for fresh fires, leapfrogging to move the fire front forward by gigantic steps, hundreds of yards at a single leap.

A few days later a blackened mountainside exposed the bare unprotected earth, torn apart by water from the rain and melting snow, waiting to be eroded. That entire holocaust could have been prevented by a few simple precautions; a shovel and a handy fire extinguisher would have been enough. Instead of that, this great new machine, with all its promise, had now wiped out the entire year's crop of that farm. More than that, it had destroyed the mountain forest and, with it, the natural watershed reservoir that should have stored the moisture for next year's crop.

Not long after that fire a world at war needed food, and paid high prices for it. More virgin land was plowed for wheat by men who didn't understand the principles of land use. Later, a great drought dried many farmlands. Whole counties of land, unwisely managed, turned into dustbowls. Millions of farmers, starving in this man-made desert, joined millions of others from the run-down and mechanized cotton lands of the South, who were streaming into the cities, searching for nonexistent jobs. Agricultural methods continued to improve, until one farmhand could produce more food than two of his predecessors, and the drift to the cities accelerated. Hungry districts in the cities turned to slums, breeding places for crime and juvenile delinquency, creating conditions which drove out earlier residents who paid taxes and created jobs.

Medicine brought the miracle of longer life and, consequently, a rapidly increasing population. These, however, brought starvation and revolt to many lands, some of them dedicated by their leaders to the destruction of the more prosperous democratic governments. Now the wheat fields held the key to life itself; hundreds of ships crossed the oceans carrying millions of tons of wheat around the world, to ward off famine and revolution, holding the line while leaders of nations sought desperately to find the road to peace and stable government.

Every man, woman, and child is living in a web whose strands reach out to the far corners of the earth. We can watch these radiating strands from the top of any New York skyscraper, with the graceful bridges pouring their streams of humanity and freight inward to fill the city, and outward to spread their strength and hopes across the nation. On the water beneath the bridges and in the air above them the ships and planes move out beyond the horizon, while others come in to take their places, carrying their millions of strands of activity to and from the far corners of the earth. They bring representatives from around the world to the United Nations, to argue, to recriminate, and to learn from each other about their mutual needs and problems. They come to search for ways of building a better human society.

A small labor union goes on strike and paralyzes traffic in the great city, disrupting the lives of millions. More than a hundred miles away a small control mechanism in a power plant fails to function, and the life of the city and its surrounding communities comes to a halt. People are stranded between stations in dark subways, in railroad trains, and in elevators. The air is filled with poisonous fumes from automobiles and smokestacks; the water is polluted from the refuse of civilization. Every life and liberty depends on the disciplined functioning of millions of other lives.

In this vast and fragile world community the problems of human relationships grow increasingly more pressing and dangerous. These, in turn, depend on the influence of chain reactions such as those set in motion long ago on a badly managed wheat field, or by a lifesaving medical discovery. The chain reactions from today's decisions thus reach out in the same way to affect tomorrow's life.

Each one of us instinctively sees this human web largely from the background of his own limited experience and interests. The hope of achieving a stable society depends on man's ability to see the picture whole and to build his future with due regard to the imperative needs of this whole. It is easy to suggest specific answers to specific problems; yet no brain has yet produced the universal catalyst, the overall solution that can bring together the vast web of intermeshed answers and translate them into effective action for world stability and peace. The first need is to understand the basic forces that today are creating problems or solutions for tomorrow.

It is more than half a century since that unforeseen spark destroyed the wheat crop and its forested watershed in Montana. In that period great minds have brought to light new understandings of life, new concepts for governing the relationships between men and nations. Great leaders have inspired men's minds with new visions for civilization. At the same time great hopes have been shattered on the hard, sharp facts of human nature; millions have given their lives to preserve those hopes, while other millions have pitted life against life to promote conflicting hopes. Human intelligence has brought to civilization many kinds of progress. The problem now is to adapt this civilization to the needs of human nature so that the two can survive together.

In this book we shall seek an understanding of the forces that make human nature what it is and that shape man's search for progress and orderly relationships with his fellows. It is a venture of exploration into a field where man is still searching for answers, a field so vast that the search may at times appear to be diffused into many unrelated subjects. We will hope that, as the search progresses, the threads of relationship will become clear as parts of an indivisible whole. Where we lack answers we hope that the search will at least serve to stimulate new questions and understanding.

acknowledgments

For reading all or parts of the manuscript and for many helpful suggestions I would like to express my appreciation to William Vogt, Richard H. Pough, William A Berridge, Carl and Harriet Buchheister, Mrs. Oliver Claxton, Roland C. Clement, Thomas Craven, Mrs. Richard W. Lloyd, and, last but not least, my wife Elizabeth and my daughter Ethel for their untiring interest and counsel.

I would also like to express thanks to Harcourt, Brace and World, Inc. for permission to quote from *The City in History*, by Lewis Mumford, in Chapter IV; and to the Population Reference Bureau for permission to use the population chart in Chapter VI.

Contents

Section I

BACKGROUND FOR TODAY

CHAPTER I

Man's Physical Environment and Biological Law

For all the fantastic qualities of the human intellect and spirit, the human body that houses them and gives them meaning is still a member of the animal kingdom, subject to the same basic laws of biology and ecology as the other living members of nature's community. The spirit that so powerfully influences both the body and the intellect is, in turn, greatly affected by other living beings as well as by the physical qualities of their environment.

Before considering man himself it may be helpful to have a look at some of these biological laws and the environment which they rule.

Like all living things, man is totally dependent on four basic natural resources: soil, water, vegetation, and animal life. As he increasingly pollutes the air he breathes, he is beginning to realize that air, too, cannot be taken for granted.

These basic resources are not separate entities, independent of each other. Each is dependent on the others for its own successful functioning. Man himself is dependent for his existence on the proper functioning of all of them, as parts of an organized whole.

Take first the fertile soil. It didn't "just happen." It is built from a base of broken particles of rock. This raw material must interact with plants, animals, and weather for thousands of years before it becomes the fertile soil that produces our crops. As plants gather energy from the sunlight and store it in their tissues, their roots spread through the soil, drawing in the minerals that have been dissolved from the rock. Vital elements are absorbed from the air and water, and using the energy from the sunlight, the plants build this combination of raw materials into their own living substance. The plants die and spread their substance on the earth's surface. Dead plants at this stage are of little use to the rest of the community, but they offer food for soil bacteria, which decompose them, breaking them into a form that other plants can then use for food. Insects and other small creatures feed on this decomposing plant matter, carrying it into their burrows and mixing it with the earth, thus giving the soil an entirely new character. This new soil contains the nutrients from the decomposed plants, together with the energy that they have gathered from the sunlight. Now it can feed the new plants that grow on its surface, producing larger vegetation.

This new addition to the soil, in turn, gives it yet another vital quality. The finely ground rock particles in most of the original soils formed a nearly waterproof surface from which the rain drained off and was wasted, but the addition of the decomposed vegetation adds a spongy consistency that helps it absorb the water. From this "sponge," the water filters downward through passageways dug by roots and small creatures to join the great natural reservoir in the earth, the source of the springs and streams that feed the farms in the fertile valleys below. These farms may depend for their existence on the distant forests and grasslands and all their animal forms that helped to store the life-giving water. These forests and grasslands and the animals that help them to function form an active, self-governing community. Like the human community it is driven by fierce competition for life and food and living space; and like a self-governing human community it is run under a sort of constitutional series of checks and balances that keeps each member in its proper place in relation to all the others. Each is able to perform its own necessary function in the life of the community, but each is prevented from overcrowding its neighbors to obstruct their proper functioning.

Like all living things, each member of this community is from time to time subject to unexpected catastrophe; drought or flood, storm, fire, or disease may wipe out large parts of the community. In order to survive, each member must have the power to reproduce itself far beyond its normal death rate to compensate for such catastrophic losses.

This reproductive power is just as dangerous as it is essential. When uncontrolled, it, too, can devastate the community. To illustrate this point, consider the soil bacteria we have just seen helping to build the fertile soil. These are among the world's smallest and yet most necessary organisms. They multiply by the simple process of dividing, each individual dividing into two complete new ones. Under favorable conditions this may take place about once every half hour.

With creatures of microscopic size this may sound rather insignificant, but watch them grow! Take a pencil and paper and see how at the end of ten hours one single ancestor will have more than two hundred and seventy-five million descendants. Ten hours later each member of this huge congregation will have multiplied itself as well by two hundred and seventy-five million.

From this point we will let the computer take over; but with each one of these ancestors continuing the same process of multiplication unchecked we are assured that they would constitute a bulk bigger than the earth in less than a week; and here is the incredible point: three quarters of all this growth would have taken place in the last hour. If our bacteria were growing in a container the size of the earth, this container would be only a quarter full at the start of the final hour, not a very ominous portent, but half an hour later, when this quarter had doubled to fill half the container, the change becomes obvious. When this again is doubled in the next half hour, the container is filled to overflowing. Long before this, the bacteria would have smothered all life on earth. Obviously this catastrophe doesn't take place. Nature controls the growth of the bacteria, as they use up their limited supply of food or crowd each other out of the more favorable areas of the soil.

This check, or control, of the reproductive process is as essential to the survival of the living community as is the original power to reproduce. Nature enforces it in various ways. Crowding beyond the carrying capacity of the environment brings hunger, disease, and conflict. Individuals crowded out of proper hiding places fall prey more easily to predators. The predator is sometimes considered an enemy of the community, but actually it is Nature's first line of defense. Its function is to keep the population within the limits that the environment can support in good health. It is when the predators fail or are absent that Nature's second line of defense comes into play, and crowding brings on hunger, disease, and competitive fighting. To survive in health, the population of the community must thus be kept in balance with the carrying capacity of the environment. This balance is seldom perfect, but it is constantly fluctuating as the opposing forces of growth and control ebb and flow around the point of balance.

We seldom notice these forces in action, but we get glimpses of them in the swoop of a hawk on its prey, or the fall of a baby robin, crowded from its nest by a stronger brother.

One large-scale demonstration of this principle has already been widely publicized, but it is so vivid and dramatic that we will venture to recall it here. It was carried out on the

Kaibab National Forest in northern Arizona. This forest, covering 700,000 acres, was good deer-hunting country. It also had its normal population of wolves, mountain lions, and coyotes, which kept the deer population in balance with its environment.

In 1905 the number of deer in the forest was estimated at about 4,000, while the area was considered capable of supporting a total of 30,000. This seemed like a fine opportunity to show what could be accomplished by proper management, yet the resulting experiment showed how little was known about proper management at that time. During the next few years 716 mountain lions, 11 wolves, and more than 7,000 coyotes were removed from the forest.

The deer began to increase until, by 1923, the herd was estimated at 100,000, far above the carrying capacity of the forest. Now, instead of wolves and mountain lions, the deer faced another problem; they were outgrowing their food supply. Instead of taking just the surplus growth from their food plants, they were forced to crop all the growth more heavily, weakening the plants that produced the growth, using up, during the summer, the entire crop of buds they would need to carry them through the winter. The deer now faced both the prospect of starvation in the cold of the coming winter and the certainty that the weakened plants would offer an inadequate supply of food for their young in the following summer.

By overusing the bounty of the forest they were actually destroying its power to support them. In effect, they were destroying the factory that produced the crop. During two severe winters, more than 60,000 deer starved to death, and, by 1939, starvation had reduced the herd to 10,000—far below the 30,000 which had been the original estimated carrying capacity of the forest.

By killing off too many of the predators which were Nature's essential controls, the managers of the forest had actually reduced its power to support the deer. This same problem is met in many of the national parks, where removal of the predators has resulted in too many deer and elk, and these now have to be removed by shooting to preserve their ranges. It is a problem, too, in many farming areas where removal of certain predators has resulted in pests of rodents and insects of many kinds.

Multiplication and control, check and balance: these are the keys to self-sustaining community life in Nature—the basis of "natural law."

There is another law in the natural community that deserves our attention; this is the law of adaptation. All living things compete for food and living space in every available niche where life can exist. Each such niche will vary somewhat from the others, and, in each one, the plants and animals that are best adapted to its own special conditions will crowd out their competitors and dominate the area. In so doing, they may sometimes change the environment so much that some new forms, better adapted to the changed environment, may come in and crowd them out. We can see this clearly in the development of a forest.

If a mature forest is cleared of all its trees, and then the seeds of those same trees are planted on the same spot, the seedlings will usually die. The environment has been so changed by the removal of the forest that its own seedlings can no longer survive on their native soil. The forest community can now rebuild itself only through a succession of steps, each one preparing the way for the next.

This land is naturally bombarded each year with millions of seeds from the trees and smaller plants that grow near it; relatively few of these seeds will survive, only those adapted to grow in the new, deforested environment that the land now provides. First must come the pioneer species to prepare the way. These will vary with local conditions of climate and soil. In the temperate climate of the northeastern United States they would be the gray birches, poplar, and white pine, together with the grasses and other small plants that can thrive in the open sunlight. These help to build the soil and protect it from erosion. Among them we would find the animals and birds that are adapted to live on the insects and vegetation of the open fields—the field mice, skunks, woodchucks, sparrows, and others.

As the pioneer trees grow they cause a change in their environment. They give shade which deprives their seedlings of the light they need for growth. But this shade makes life possible for other kinds of trees whose seedlings require some protection from the direct sunlight: the tulip, red maple, red oak, and white ash, among others. This second group of trees, in its turn, will grow and produce a deeper shade, so dense that the seedlings of the earlier pioneer trees will die for lack of sunlight, and these pioneer forms will therefore eventually disappear from the forest. They are wiped out by the changes in their environment that they themselves have produced.

As the trees of the second group grow and shade the forest floor even more deeply, their own seedlings will suffer in their turn until they also die, to be replaced at last by the shade-tolerant trees such as the hemlock, beech, and sugar maple. These will form a shade so dense that no other trees can compete with them under the conditions that they have established. No birds or other animals can live here that are not adapted to this moist, heavily shaded environment and to the food that it produces. Except around the forest openings, the animal community of the open fields has gone. This dark environment can no longer feed and support them. This is the more or less permanent "climax" forest that dominates all life in the environment it has established.

The so-called climax forest, for all its dominance, is a very delicately balanced "organism." The fate of the lordly trees depends on the cooperation of many other members of the community. Prominent among these are the invisible soil bacteria that we have already mentioned. The smallest members of the community, they play a vital role in supporting the life of the forest. Through the years the dead leaves and trees fall to the ground. This dead vegetation is important to the life of the forest. But, in its original condition, it is not merely useless, it is actually a hazard to the forest. It must first be changed into a new form that both the trees and the soil can use.

We have already seen how the bacteria and molds, billions of them to each cubic inch, break up the dead vegetation through the processes of decay and make it available to the trees for food.

To understand the meaning of this change we will travel a few miles north, to the northern borders of the climax hemlock forest in Alaska. Here the climate average is a few degrees colder, the hours of sunlight a few minutes shorter. Botanists do not know all the effects of this change, but it does affect the activity of the soil bacteria. In this environment they function just a bit less effectively. They cannot keep up with the supply of leaves and dead wood that falls to the forest floor.

The debris accumulates, building a deep layer of spongy, acid peat. The forest floor becomes a sponge, filled with acid water that cuts off the roots from the mineral soil beneath. This is, then, no longer a self-perpetuating forest; in this new environment the forest can no longer survive. The weaker trees die, leaving open spots where bogs of peat and sphagnum moss have developed. Around them stand the gaunt moss-draped skeletons of dead and dying hemlocks. The forest is dying in the new environment that it has created, but it still fights for survival. The surface of the bog is dotted with the sickly dying seedlings of hemlocks that have failed in their attempt to carry on the lives of their ancestors. Among them stand occasional gnarled skeletons of their fellows that have fought their way to a height of four or five feet before giving up the struggle. Their nearly microscopic growth rings tell us that this losing fight has sometimes lasted for as long as seventy-five to a hundred years before the final defeat. This forest had destroyed itself through the failure of its smallest supporting members to adapt themselves to the changes in the environment, and the forest thus at last evolves into a treeless tundra where no forest can grow. We can at last see the interaction between life and its environment. The living things act to change their environment, and, with this change, the environment, in its turn, acts to select the things that are best adapted to survive under the conditions it imposes.

On one of these Alaskan bogs, we came across a corduroy road of logs on whose surface someone had spread gravel. Passing cars had splashed some of this gravel onto the surface of the bog. Here, in this dying community, the gravel had supplied the mineral foundation for a new community of pioneer plants: willow, alder, spruce, and others. The principles involved in this saga of life and death deserve more attention from man, as he busily bulldozes his way through his own environment. What unrecognized forces as simple as the tree shadows on the earth, or as invisible as the bacteria, is he setting in motion toward changing the conditions that govern his own existence? What essential requirements for the nourishment of his body and spirit may he be destroying in this new and unaccustomed environment?

CHAPTER II

Self-government in Nature

The biological laws discussed in the last chapter impose a stern code of behavior on every form of animal life. Their application is automatic, and obedience is the key to survival. The rabbit that trusts the fox learns his lesson too late to benefit by it. The swallow that lingers too long in the North will not survive the changed conditions imposed by the winter environment.

These creatures have the ability to learn but little opportunity. The key to their survival lies in the instincts that they have inherited from a distant past. Through these instincts the members of the animal community enjoy a form of automatic self-government that regulates their relations to each other and to the rest of their environment.

In our vastly more complicated world community, we have also been searching for some form of self-government that will meet the requirements for stability in a world of new and contrasting ideas. We do not seem very close to a solution. Before we begin to consider our own problems, it might be helpful to take a look at some of these simpler forms. Here we may find resemblances to some of our human problems. Perhaps we may locate ways to improve on the principles that we see here and adapt them to the human picture.

Wherever in the world we are fortunate enough to have songbirds in the spring, we enjoy their first notes as the nesting season approaches. The singer, no doubt, is enjoying the sunshine and the bountiful supply of food, but his song is serious business, an important part of his struggle for survival. He is singing not so much for the joy of it, but to tell all other males of his species that this is his private territory, which they must not enter. As a rule, this private territory is of a size and quality needed both to feed his prospective family and to provide the necessary shelter from predators and the weather. Any competitor of the same species who wants to use this territory will have to fight for it, and there will be no mating until final ownership has been established. Later, when the females come along, they will mate with the victors who have established ownership of the nesting grounds.

The nesting is confined to the number of birds that the land can adequately feed and shelter, and these, through the selective process of competition, will on the average be the strongest and best qualified to pass on their inheritance of vigor to the next generation. Meanwhile the unmated birds will perform a role of secondary usefulness. Deprived of the best territories, they will be more vulnerable to predators whose attention will thus be diverted from the more important nesting families. The survivors, meanwhile, form a reserve from which new mates may be acquired in case of death among the mated pairs. There is, of course, no hard and fast line at which nesting stops. However, between the opposing forces of surging competing life and what is called environmental resistance, a rough working balance is achieved between the population and the carrying capacity of the environment. The community is thereby protected from overcrowding. The best and ablest males are selected to pass on their good qualities to the next generation, and order is thus maintained in the community. This might appear to be a splendid example of intelligence in the management of relationships within the group. But such "intelligence" shows itself to lie not so much within the conscious choice of the individual bird, as in the deep-seated instinct inherited from distant ancestors.

Robert Ardrey, in his far-reaching study of territorial behavior, finds this instinct to be one of the key underlying forces that regulate the interrelationships of animals, with each other and with the rest of their environment. This instinct is widespread throughout the vertebrate world. It takes many forms. Each territorial species has its own special form that probably has some survival value for its own way of life.

The herring gull, in its crowded colony, will fiercely defend the three or four feet of space immediately surrounding its nest. But what is the gull defending? The Laysan albatross suggested the answer in the course of its famous contest with the U.S. Navy over territorial rights on Midway Island in the Pacific Ocean. With 60,000 pairs of albatross nesting on the island, the airborne birds became a menace to the jet planes over the landing strips. In search of a solution, the Navy undertook a study of the birds with the help of scientists from the U.S. Fish and Wildlife Service.

The albatross appears to be a fine example of family devotion. It mates for life, coming together for the nesting season, then separating to spread out over the ocean for the rest of the year. As part of the study, a hundred pairs of the birds were marked, and a record kept of the exact location of the nest of each pair. The following season ninety-five of these pairs returned to nest within thirteen feet of the site of the previous year's nest, although in most cases, the remains of that nest had been wiped out by the weather.

In another test, eighteen of the birds were marked with distinctive colors and transported to distant shores of the Pacific. Fourteen returned, including two that covered the 3,100 miles from Puget Sound in ten and twelve days respectively. They seemed eager to get back to their families; but when the Navy undertook to build a new installation at the base, it became necessary to move some of the nests. A hundred of the nests were moved, each with its live chick, to distances of up to a hundred yards, and then the bulldozers went to work to clean up the area. The displaced parents, which had been devotedly caring for their young, now sat on the edge of the clearing watching the bulldozers, and their abandoned chicks all finally died. Day after day, when the bulldozers retired for the night, the parents returned to the empty site where the nests had been, apparently driven like automatons by some inner force. For these albatross the young no longer existed when they lost their identification with the all-important patch of home territory.

An experiment reported by Dr. Konrad Lorenz helps to shed some light on this strange behavior. He has pointed out that the dividing line between instinct and intelligence is not a simple one, and that instinct itself may represent a complex interrelationship of forces in which motivations and inhibitions interact to modify each other. In many cases the aggressive instinct is the basic motivation, but it may be modified or redirected to produce peaceful results, as in the case of the mother turkey.

The turkey hen is a devoted mother and will aggressively defend her brood, attacking anything, up to the size of a cat, that moves near her nest. But, in an experiment with some deaf turkey hens it was found that, instead of defending their young poults, they pecked them to death as soon as they were hatched. In further experiments with turkeys that had normal hearing, a stuffed poult was dragged toward a brooding mother by a long string. Again the mother attacked it vigorously. Then the stuffed poult was equipped with a loudspeaker which transmitted a taped recording of the notes of a new-hatched poult. On hearing this sound the mother turkey welcomed the poult with typical maternal notes. The same experiment was tried using a stuffed weasel in place of the poult, and with the same results. In a further test the mother was approached by a voiceless dummy poult, and by a stuffed polecat which carried the identifying voice recording. She pecked furiously at the voiceless chick, but welcomed the crying polecat, calling to it as she allowed it to move under her.

In this case, the maternal instinct would seem to have been divided into two parts: first the aggressive drive, which led to attacks against any moving object within the defended territory, and, second, the maternal response to a particular sound, whether it came from offspring or enemy. This was true chiefly for inexperienced mothers with their first brood.

Ardrey also refers to a study of rhesus monkeys by Dr. C. R. Carpenter. This monkey lives in groups, in India, each group defending its own territory against all others of its kind. The typical group may include five or six males, each with his family of wives and young, usually with one or two dominant males acting as leaders. Dr. Carpenter collected a group of 350 rhesus monkeys from different parts of India, so that they would be strangers without any social organization. They were shipped to the thirty-six-acre island of Santiago in the Caribbean. In the course of the sea voyage there was no sign of order or group responsibility among them. Each individual fought for its own food, mothers even fighting their young. No males assumed responsibility for the welfare of their families. In the course of the voyage ten of the young died.

The monkeys were freed on the island, and food was supplied regularly by a caretaker. There was no need to compete for food or for the territory that would produce it. During most of the first year in their new home, the monkeys remained in their state of disorganized anarchy, and more young were killed by adults than by all other causes.

Finally, toward the end of the year, the colony began to settle down to a more orderly way of life and divided itself into permanent groupings. Each group selected its own separate territory, which it defended against all others, just as would occur in the wild. The members of each group were friendly and cooperative with their fellow members but hostile to all outsiders. Again the mothers took care of their young, and infant mortality dropped to normal. The organized social way of life, based on a familiar and defended home territory, seemed to have been a basic instinctive need for the success of the community—even with an assured food supply and no danger from predators. While each group stoutly defended its own defined territory from intrusion, there was no organized attempt by any of the groups to intrude on the territory of its neighbors.

It is interesting that, even with the freedom of the island, the conditions and the food supply were not entirely natural. The reaction of the monkeys was thus not entirely typical. In their wild state, these monkeys may occasionally shift their territory. The antagonism between the separate groups may be just as extreme, but the emphasis is more on the defense of the group than on the defense of territory. Among the different species of monkey there is a wide variation in their methods of group and territorial defense.

Some interesting studies have been made of the chacma baboon in its native surroundings. Here we have a vivid picture of the real value and the evolutionary background of territoriality and group organization. The baboon, a ground dweller, lacking the claws, the teeth, and the fleetness of foot to match the larger predators, is extremely vulnerable and is a favorite food of the leopard. Against such an enemy the single baboon is helpless. But he finds safety in organized numbers, and he lives in groups that may range from one hundred to three hundred or more. To survive, this group must control enough territory to supply the necessary food and shelter for its own needs.

By day such a group will command enough watchful eyes and fighting strength to discourage the appetites of its enemies. As the group moves out to feed, the old males take up positions on the outskirts and also form a guard in the rear. When the group stops to rest or feed, a sentinel or two keep watch for the approach of danger. With the exception of the real leader, these are often the largest and strongest males. When these sentinels give warning of approaching danger, the leader will assemble the leading males along the sides and rear of the party (with the females and young in the middle or at the front), while he himself takes a position at the front or the rear, as conditions may dictate. In case of actual attack, the young are defended even at great risk to the adults. By day, the troop is fairly safe from all enemies but man; by night it faces a completely different problem.

Robert Ardrey, in his book *African Genesis,* tells of a study by Eugene Marais, who spent three years living among a troop of baboons, winning their confidence, and learning to know them individually. There were several groups in the area.

One group, especially fortunate, owned a cave 500 feet up on the face of a cliff, which could be approached only by a narrow ledge. In this impregnable fortress the group was safe through the hours of darkness. Other groups were not so fortunate. In the absence of shelter their lives depended on finding hiding places among the hillside rocks. Those that could find safe shelter survived the terror-filled nights, whereas the less fortunate became easy prey for the leopard. Thus, a balance was maintained between the death rate and the birth rate, and the population was maintained at about the level that the territory of each group could feed and protect; moreover, the population of predators was limited to the number that could subsist on the surplus animals.

One evening, as Mr. Marais watched his baboon friends returning to their rocky hillside, a leopard appeared at dusk, before the members of the troop had settled into their hiding places. The leopard watched the terror-stricken troop scrambling for shelter, perhaps waiting to locate some exposed victim. As it watched from a rock just below a small jutting cliff, two male baboons edged along the top of the cliff above it. Then, together, they dropped onto the leopard. One bit at its spine while the other seized its throat.

In an instant, the leopard had disemboweled one of the attackers with its hind claws and crushed the other with its jaws; but the dying, disembowelled baboon held on long enough to reach the jugular vein. Both predator and prey died together. We may be justified in asking ourselves whether these baboons showed a reasoned response, an almost human sense of responsibility, in giving their lives voluntarily for the good of the community. Or was this an automatic, instinctive reaction to the sight of the leopard in a vulnerable position? We cannot know.

Obviously many of the higher animals can give what appears to be a reasoned, flexible response to a new situation. In an earlier book, *The Web of Life* (Signet, New York, 1953), I mentioned a personal experience in which I watched through field glasses as a family of ground squirrels outmaneuvered a wire cage trap. After seeing the door of the trap close behind two of their number, the others would no longer take the obvious entrance to get at the bait; yet they were still cautiously interested in reaching it, and they were willing to investigate further. They tested the wire netting on all sides of the trap with their teeth, then one of them dug his way under the trap and pulled the bait down between the wires. It would be hard to maintain that this did not show both reason and imagination in an animal which, at the same time, is governed by a strong territorial instinct.

The important point to remember is that, even with the gift of reason, a large part of animal life is governed automatically by instinct. In man, of course, instinct comes largely under the control of reason, and because of this, many thoughtful people have felt that instinct in man can have little in common with instinct in other animals. Certainly there are many typical human actions which in any other animal would qualify as instincts. We see them in human aggressiveness, attachment to territory, the striving for dominance and rank, mob psychology, and so on.

Konrad Lorenz, in *On Aggression*, mentions one tendency in man which appears to be shared chiefly with the rat and certain insects. This is the drive toward aggressive destruction against members of the same species who are not members of the same community. It is a drive which might tend toward race suicide in contrast to the territorial and aggressive instincts of other animals that tend to maintain peace and order within their own species.

In an experiment with brown rats, F. Steiniger put groups

of ten or fifteen rats, strangers from different areas, into a large enclosure under perfectly natural living conditions. At first they seemed rather shy of each other, and not inclined to fight. But they gradually became more aggressive and began to compete for territories. In some cases, several pairs would form at the same time and among these pairs there would be fighting that might continue for a long time. But, if one pair formed ahead of the others, this pair would team up to take possession of the territory and harass all the others until they killed them, usually within two or three weeks. As the offspring of the victorious pair multiplied, the members of the resulting tribe remained peaceable among themselves. If a strange rat was introduced into this colony, there was no disturbance until one of the colony members came near enough to smell the strange scent. Then, at a cry or signal from this member, the whole colony would become very excited. The members attacked each other on meeting until, by sniffing, they could verify that each had the proper home scent. Finally, after the whole colony had identified the stranger, it would turn on him en masse and tear him to pieces. Evidently the stranger was identified only by smell, and this smell aroused the instinct which automatically doomed the nonmember of the group. If a regular member of the tribe was taken from the colony and put in another enclosure until it lost the "colony scent," it would be attacked, just like any other stranger, when it was returned to the colony. If, however, it was placed in an enclosure with soil and nest material from the colony until it reacquired the "colony scent," it was again accepted as a member. The scent was as automatically effective with the rats as the recorded voice was with the turkeys.

Dr. Lorenz indicates that this form of social order in the rat "represents a model in which we can see some of the dangers threatening ourselves." It might be difficult to prove that this was basically different from those group prejudices that appear so often in man, where the colony scent may take the form of skin color, religion, or status.

It is often contended that such prejudice is the result of the teaching or the example of elders. On this point Ardrey speaks of the Eskimo dogs of eastern Greenland. These animals live in packs, and each pack vigorously defends its own social territory. Tinbergen noticed that the immature males do not recognize the territorial boundaries, frequently crossing them and being severely punished for the infraction. They seem unable to learn until they reach maturity. Then they quickly learn and carefully observe the boundaries. Does this suggest something more than teaching?

The cumulative evidence of fossil discoveries makes it unmistakably clear that man has evolved from the animal community. A major human problem today is to understand the implications of this background and to find ways of adapting it to the needs of civilization.

CHAPTER III

The Human Inheritance

From the mists of controversy that have surrounded the study of evolution, one fact seems clear: the fossil records tell us that man is not descended from any living species of ape. Both appear to be descended from an intermediate great-grandparent. With all his superior qualities, man appears to be merely the highest level yet reached by the great unending stream of life that has been passed on through one living form to the next for many hundred million years.

As the living stream advances, each new reproductive cell carries within itself certain inherited codes or instructions. When male and female mate, each partner contributes to the union a collection of genes which carry the different qualities that have been inherited from the forebears of the past. From this grab-bag of genes each offspring receives a share allotted to it by chance, half of the total coming from each parent. This living spark absorbs elements from the earth, air, and water, plus energy from the sunlight, and builds them into the form that has been pre-ordained by the genetic instructions that it received through its parents.

Occasionally some mutation will affect the inherited genetic code, and an individual appears with a new or changed characteristic that can be passed on to the next generation. Some of these changes are advantageous for their owner, and thus new forms evolve which are better adapted to win their place in the struggle for survival. Other changes are not so helpful, and their owners are eliminated by the hazards of their environment.

Thus, environment automatically affects the course of evolution, selecting and encouraging the development of living forms that are best adapted to survive under the conditions it imposes. At the same time it eliminates others that are less fitted to cope with its hazards. A familiar and much simplified example of this type of selection is the performance of the salt marsh mosquito when its home environment is sprayed with DDT. The poisoned environment is quite effective in eliminating the mosquito, but there are often a few individuals with the inherited capacity to withstand the poison. With all competitors eliminated by the poison, the immune survivors now produce a new colony that inherits the DDT-resistant quality.

The fossil records make it clear that man did not become human by a single evolutionary step. He evolved through a long series of steps, so gradual that it is difficult to pinpoint the dividing line between man and ape. A number of fossil remains with a combination of apelike and human characteristics have been found in southern Africa. The skull base and hip and leg bones show that the owner walked upright, like a man, but otherwise the creature had the characteristics of an ape. The skull had the small brain capacity of a gorilla, ranging from 450 to 650 cubic centimeters, compared with an average range of 1,200 to 1,600 for Neanderthal and recent man. The teeth, jaws, and chewing-muscle bases were adapted for the vegetarian diet of the ape; no living species of ape, however, is built to walk with the erect carriage of man. Another type of fossil had the erect carriage and small brain, but the skull, jaws, and teeth showed some major changes. They were not built for the heavy chewing demanded by the vegetarian diet of the ape; the muscle bases were built to carry smaller chewing muscles, and the teeth were better adapted for the carnivorous or omnivorous diet of man.

Associated with these fossil remains were pieces of stone that had been chipped or flaked to form crude tools for scraping or cutting. Tests at the University of California, using the potassium-argon method, have given an age of about 1,750,000 years for these remains, although there has been some criticism of the accuracy of this testing method.* While there is no proof that these tools were made by the

---

* The gas Argon-40 is formed by the decay of potassium-40. When a crystalline mineral containing potassium-40 is heated to 500° F. or more, the Argon-40 previously formed within it escapes. After the mineral cools, new Argon-40 atoms collect inside it at a fixed rate. Thus, minerals such as anorthoclase, which have been heated in a volcanic eruption, contain Argon-40 that has been accumulating at a fixed rate, only since the time of the eruption. The measurement of the proportion of Argon-40

small-brained ape-men (Australopithecus), no remains of large-brained Homo sapiens have been found associated with the tools. The circumstantial evidence therefore strongly indicates that the tools came before the brain growth.

Fossils of these early Australopithecine ape-men have been found at several sites in Africa. They vary somewhat at the different sites. This suggests that they lived and developed without much intermixing, separated by distance or geographical barriers and different methods of living. The small available evidence suggests that there was a greater difference between these family groups or bands than there is today between the different races of men.

In Java, the fossil remains of an upward step in human progress were found. This early man had a low forehead and skull vault, with the heavy brow ridges of his predecessors, but his brain capacity had grown to average about 900 cubic centimeters, about halfway between Australopithecus and modern man. This Java man has been called *Homo erectus*. Above him, in the evolutionary sense, came Neanderthal man with a brain size ranging between 1,200 and 1,600 cc.—equal to modern man, but with a very different skull shape, longer and lower than modern man, and with no real chin. His remains are found chiefly in Europe, but specimens have also come from such widely scattered areas as North Africa, Palestine, Iraq, and Turkestan. Like his predecessors, he too finally became extinct.

About 35,000 years ago, modern man appeared in Europe. There are two caves at Mount Carmel, in Palestine, where skulls were found that showed characteristics of both Neanderthal and modern man, leading to the suggestion that there may have been some interbreeding which led to the development of modern man.

There are many intermediate variations between the types we have mentioned here, and much speculation and difference of opinion as to their interrelationships. As Professor Ernst Mayr pointed out in 1963, new finds in this field are coming so rapidly that any inferences drawn today may well be invalidated within a short time. On three points, however, the evidence does appear conclusive: first, man did not appear on earth as a new, special creation. He arose through the normal process of evolution—a long series of steps. Sec-

within the mineral thus tells, within a margin of error of 5 to 7 percent, how long ago the volcano erupted. This, in turn, under the right conditions, helps to give the age of the detritus beds in which fossils are found. (See C. S. Coon, *The Origin of Races*, p. 313.)

ond, in the evolution from ape to human, all of the human physical characteristics were pretty well developed before the brain started to grow. It seems probable that these physical developments supplied the selective pressures that led to the evolution of the brain. The upright carriage opened the way for the development of the breathing apparatus to allow better control of the voice; it also freed the hands for other useful activities besides locomotion. The ability to feed without using the snout to pick up food thus opened the way for the development of the mouth and tongue for speech.

In this defenseless, unarmed creature, no longer living in the protecting trees and depending on the hunt for a good share of his food, the pressures of the environment would have tended to select for survival the superior individuals. While these pressures demanded physical strength, they especially required the intelligence to make use of the new opportunities that evolution had provided. The man with the imagination to devise speech, to visualize and communicate thought, to make plans, and to organize and lead his fellows became the most valuable member of his group and contributed most to its survival.

Finally we come to the third point of certainty. All living human beings are considered to be of the same species: Homo sapiens. All can interbreed and all form a single set of intercommunicating gene pools. With the exception of identical twins no two individuals are alike. From the vast pool of genetic qualities no two draw exactly the same combination. Where different groups have been separated for a long time without interbreeding some have developed their own special characteristics helped by the selective pressures of their environment. Different climates may favor different skin colors. In the thick forest, size may be a handicap; the environment thus favors the pigmy. The Alakaluf Indians of Tierra del Fuego were able to fish and hunt without clothing in freezing weather and to dive for shellfish in icy water. They had developed a basal metabolism 160 percent higher than the normal for whites of the same size.

The widespread separation of the different groups is attested to by the fact that there are thousands of different languages, hundreds of which are unrelated to each other. There is enough difference in the skeletons of the different races so that a good anatomist can distinguish between them. The weight of scientific evidence, however, seems to indicate that the average person of any race has as much capacity for learning as the average individual of any other race, given the same educational and environmental background. The creative imagination of Einstein and Beethoven, the gentle unselfishness of Christ, the bloodthirsty savagery of Hitler, and the whole range of intermediate variations down to the mental incompetent would seem to imply that there is as much variation within races as there is between races. Professor Mayr states that the differences between individuals of a single population or race are usually larger than those between populations or races.

This wide range of potentials makes up the raw material of human society. Man's problem is to learn how to make the best use of these potentials and develop an environment where they can flourish. In his aggressiveness, territorial exclusiveness, prejudices, and many other traits, man gives good evidence that he is still largely guided by those ancient instincts that served him so well when he was still wholly a member of the animal community. With the development of mind, hand, and power of speech, he has now built an environment where those instincts, undisciplined, become suicidal. The slow, harsh processes of evolution do not offer a hopeful solution for man in his search for civilization. The key to such a hope now lies in the development of his culture, the shaping of tradition, habits of thought, and motivations. At bottom this becomes a race between intelligence and outworn instincts.

CHAPTER IV

Civilizations and Deserts

Human life today is oppressed and distorted by the inherited mistakes of history. We can see a clearer picture of human nature if we watch it searching for civilization in its unspoiled primeval environment.

It was more than 17,000 centuries from the time when the ape-man made his first stone tools until the first evidence of dawning civilization appeared. Through that long interval man left few tangible records of progress. The changing size and shape of his head showed that his mental equipment was growing. The improving quality of his stone tools and weapons showed that he was putting this growing brain to work and that he was passing the results on to his offspring for the improvement of his culture.

In his caves, man was leaving the bones of animals he used for food. Changes in the types of these bones showed that he was developing skills as a hunter. The earliest bone collections showed that he was catching small, slow-moving animals. Later, the bones of larger, stronger animals showed that he was both improving his skills as a hunter and probably hunting in organized groups.

About 360,000 years ago, in a cave in Choukoutien, China, Pekin man left the remains of fire, together with the broken and roasted bones of his fellow man. The use of fire must have given man a tremendous advantage in his struggle against cold and predatory animals and in his ability to prepare food and to use a wider variety of edible things. It lengthened his day through the hours when he could not be hunting outdoors, thus expanding his social life and his chances for planning and thought. The beautiful cave paintings of France and Spain tell us that, thousands of centuries later, he was already using his intelligence and imagination to create beauty and to convey ideas and knowledge.

Somewhere in this vast expanse of time he made one of his greatest forward steps when he used that imagination to organize sounds into meaning. With words he could not only visualize and clarify his own thinking, he could also exchange thoughts with his fellows and organize group action. Finally, between 10,000 and 9000 B.C., a few groups of the early men groped their way toward the great step that was to revolutionize human life. They discovered how to farm the earth, to make it produce more food, especially the cereals which could be stored for future use; they learned to domesticate animals that could turn the products of the earth into meat and bone, wool and leather.

It has been estimated that an average human family, living by hunting and the gathering of wild foods, will require between ten and fifty square miles of land (depending on its productiveness), for their support. On the other hand, a farmer settled on rich, well-watered land like the Nile Valley can produce enough to support a thousand people per square mile. The knowledge of agriculture gave human life a new meaning. It was able to give man an entirely new relationship to his environment, including his fellow man—the most important part of that environment.

As a hunter requiring a large territory, man was necessarily limited to living in small groups, each defending its own territory and rejecting additions beyond a tolerable size. He had not yet evolved as a creature adapted for life in a large community. But with his ability to raise food in quantity, he was drawn by many forces into living in larger communities, and this raised some new problems.

The Near East, in those early days, offered resources that were especially favorable for the development of agriculture. Here there grew the ancestral forms of wheat and barley that could be bred into rich sources of food. Here also lived the wild ancestors of animals that would respond to domestication—the sheep, goat, pig, cattle, and wild ass—which were to be found in the uplands bordering the Syrian desert at altitudes of about 2,000 to 3,000 feet. At least three, possibly more, centers of human development began on the western slopes and valleys of the Zagros Mountains that border western Iran, in the hill country of Turkish Mesopotamia and on the South Anatolian Plateau. There is still much excavating and research to be done in this country. All of the ancient remains so far discovered indicate that, up to about 10,000 B.C., the people who lived here depended entirely on hunting and food-gathering for their subsistence.

Among the oldest ancient ruins is Jericho. It was occupied nearly continuously for several thousand years. In its different levels of occupation, the artifacts and other clues to human activities help to suggest some of the important steps in the development of its early culture. The site of what might have been a shrine shows a radiocarbon date of 9551 B.C.; the settlement grew up near an abundant spring. Stone tools and weapons indicate that, in the beginning, hunting and fishing still supplied a considerable part of the food. But sickle blades and querns, for grinding grain, indicate that plant foods were also being used. Clay-lined pits suggest the storage of foods as well. (It is interesting to note that, even with the availability of clay and fire, it was still to be thousands of years before the art of pottery-making was developed.)

At first Jericho was a small village with houses built of clay. During the 8th millennium B.C., it began to grow rapidly, which suggests that, by this time, agriculture, with the help of hunting and the gathering of wild foods, had become productive enough to support a growing population. Through the centuries the houses went through many phases of building and then rebuilding over the ruins of the old—the types of building changing as the years passed. At this time there was still no pottery, and during this prepottery era at Jericho there were twenty-two separate phases of building that could be distinguished in the excavations.

During the first three building phases, the town had no fortifications. Evidently, unhappy experience showed the need for protection, and tremendous efforts were later put into the building of fortifications. About 7100 B.C., the settlement was destroyed by fire. Following this there were four more rebuildings, and then the site was apparently deserted for a time. It has been estimated from the size of the ruins that the population of Jericho must at one time have reached about 2,000. The huge amount of labor that went into the erection and maintenance of the fortifications implies not only that there was an ample available labor force, but that there must have been an effective leadership to organize and direct it. To feed such a community there must have been a productive system of agriculture, and it is thought likely that there must have been some outside source of revenue, such as trade. The presence of nephrite and other green stones, together with sulphur, bitumen, salt, shells, and turquoise matrix suggests such sources of origin as the Dead Sea, the Red Sea, Sinai, and Anatolia.

Early in the 7th millennium B.C. a new culture was brought to the deserted site of Jericho. This occupation must have lasted for a long time. In some places there were as many as twenty-six layers of plaster floors superimposed one above the other. There were indications of concern with the supernatural.

There were shrines and many small figurines of animals and of the mother goddess associated with a fertility cult. There were a number of human skulls that may have been associated with an ancestor cult. The faces were modeled in plaster, with cowrie shells for eyes. Some were painted to represent hair, and in one case a face was supplied with a mustache. This prepottery period lasted well into the 6th millennium B.C. It was succeeded by a totally different culture that used pottery for the first time.

As new settlements arose with their local differences the remnants left by the human occupants helped to show the steps in cultural development. The spread of the different types of pottery helped to indicate the trade routes and outlined the interchange of cultural contacts. About the middle of the 5th millennium B.C. cast copper tools and weapons appeared, followed a little later by gold. It would be, however, some centuries before the advent of the age of bronze.

By 4000 B.C. villages were growing to the status of city-states, and with this growth came the need for better means of organization and government. This need may have been the inspiration for a system of writing. By about 3500 B.C. written documents began to appear in Mesopotamia. Based at first on pictographs, the script developed by the Sumerians evolved into systematic writing, and, with this, the enrichment of knowledge and thought and the enrichment of human culture took another great forward step. Knowledge and ideas could now be accumulated and communicated. Organization and control of great masses of people thus became possible.

The development of the cities brought with it a basic change in human relationships that has been plaguing mankind with increasing intensity ever since. The early villages were made up of small groups of families, each with its own hearth, its own household god, with its social structure built around the small, intimate group. Lewis Mumford points out that "what we call morality began in the mores, the life-conserving customs of the village. When these primary bonds dissolve, when the intimate community ceases to be a watchful . . . deeply concerned group, then the 'we' becomes a buzzing swarm of 'I's.' "

The mixing together of many peoples with different tribal customs brought confusion and lawlessness and the need for enforced laws to maintain order. Laws were enforced with savage cruelties, including mutilation, drowning, and burning to death. Professor Mumford points out that this legalized violence was not a holdover from an even more vicious past; it was a new kind of ferocity peculiar to urban culture. Throughout history the depersonalization, divisions, and constraints within the city have produced undercurrents of tension and rebellion. With these came the need for laws to regulate the relationships between the individual and society.

Brutality, however, was an ineffective instrument for the winning of loyalty, and the early rulers therefore relied heavily on the development of religious beliefs to strengthen their authority. At this time in Mesopotamia the three chief deities were: Anu, god of the sky; Enki or Ea, god of wisdom and of the water, the creator and organizer of all that is good in the world; and Enlil, god of the air and the storm—he was the agent who carried out the decisions of the other gods and was therefore responsible, not only for the organization of prosperity, but also for any necessary destructions such as a flood or the sack of a city. The other great power of the universe was the earth, Ninmah or Ninhursag, wife of heaven, mother of all the gods, and the source of all life and fertility, made to conceive by the power of water. Beneath these great deities was the hierarchy of lesser gods, each with his or her special function, covering all aspects of human life. They were concerned, apparently, with life as it is lived by ordinary human beings, not so much with setting standards or trying to make people better.

Each city-state was the property of a god, and his status in the hierarchy fluctuated with the fortunes of his city. Enlil, however, retained his central executive function at all times and his city, Nippur, was always the major holy city of the area. Enlil was a national rather than a local god, and through him the Sumerians, even though politically divided, gained a sense of nationality and kinship.

The people of southern Mesopotamia considered that their lands and their persons were owned by their gods. They believed that man had been created for one purpose only—to serve the gods and save them the trouble of working for themselves. The houses of the community tended to concentrate around the house that was built for the local god. Thus, the wealth and skills of the community came together around the religious center.

The land around the temple was owned by its god, but each man had a plot of land to support himself, and he also helped to work the god's land and maintain his canals. The priests, too, had their allotments of land and their duties. Tools and seeds were supplied by the temple, and the chief priest exercised the overall control of the temple community. The political government of the community was exercised by a council of elders. In time of emergency supreme power could be delegated temporarily to one leader who served only for the time of the crisis.

As the cities grew in size and overlapped their boundaries, the central city might thus acquire more than one god with his temple community. With increasing size there also came the problem of maintaining peace between the cities. The first thousand years of recorded history give a rather kaleidoscopic picture of struggles for power and growth, and, with continuing emergencies, the idea of temporary power for the chosen leaders gave way to the seizure of permanent power and kingship.

About 2400 B.C. a canal system was built that connected the Tigris and Euphrates rivers. This greatly increased the area of irrigated farming as well as the opportunities for trade and conquest.

The increasing contacts between the cities brought new problems into focus. Religion, represented by both an ever-present god and a semidivine king, was a powerful stabilizing force within the city. But in relations with the gods of other cities the city god was less helpful. As Professor Mumford has pointed out: "In the early days at least in Mesopotamia and Egypt the gods were all mad-mad with the lust of power, the desire to control." "On the favored terms desired by gods and kings, no city could secure its own expansion except by ruining and destroying other cities." "Who was the enemy? Anyone who worshipped another god, who rivaled the king's powers or resisted the king's will."

In 2331 B.C. a powerful king, Sargon, set out to build an empire, conquering a huge area from the Persian Gulf to the Taurus Mountains and the Mediterranean. Throughout a reign of almost fifty years, he was engaged in almost continuous warfare, dealing with revolts, and attempting to establish peace and unity in the empire. He founded his own city of Akkad and attempted to rule by force, spreading garrisons over the land, tearing down the protecting walls of competing cities, and taking hostages. But the use of force only led to more revolts, and he later tried to build the personal loyalty of his subjects. He kept Nippur as the religious center and established a civil service of Akkadian citizens who served under a personal oath of loyalty to himself. The men who controlled the provinces and other important positions were all appointed from this group. Thus, toward the end of his reign, he succeeded in establishing a period of great prosperity with widespread trade and commerce.

But human relationships were still largely a matter of force and the exercise of personal leadership. For the next four hundred years the development of the region fluctuated between times of success and decay. Two great kings, Shulgi and Naramsin, were deified for their successful reigns, which included the building of canals and temples and the maintenance of order; even during these times of prosperity the region was under constant pressure from tribes of nomads who grazed their flocks in the uplands to the east and north. Seeking new grazing lands for their sheep and goats, waves of invaders spread into the country, fighting for control of the land, cutting off cities from their sources of food and from their trade routes. Thus, between the times of prosperity, there were periods of economic collapse and famine. Canals became filled with silt, farms deteriorated, and cities were destroyed or abandoned. Within a period of three years four different kings sat on the throne of Sargon's city of Akkad. Finally, in 2151 B.C., it was attacked by invading Gutians and destroyed so thoroughly that its site has never been discovered.

In 1894 B.C. a new force was born in Mesopotamia. A small religious center, which later came to be known as Babylon, lay between the Tigris and Euphrates. It had a favorable position for trade and agriculture, and the rivers made good defensive barriers on each side. A wall was built around the city together with a number of outlying fortresses. Through years of campaigning and the conquest and destruction of competing cities, the power of Babylon grew. During this turbulent century there was one period of twenty-four years when the neighboring holy city of Nippur "changed hands" no less than eighteen times.

In 1793 B.C. Hammurabi inherited the throne of Babylon. Destined to become one of the great monarchs of antiquity, he devoted the early years of his reign to building the strength of the city, carrying out internal reforms, rebuilding the canals that supplied water for neighboring cities and allying himself with some to conquer others. When the usefulness of an ally was ended, he might turn on it and defeat it (as in the case of Larsa) or destroy it when it failed to abide by the terms of a treaty.

In attempting to unify his empire, he found that an important problem lay in the diversity of religious beliefs. The Semitic sun-worship, for example, was alien to the nature religion of the Sumerians. Hammurabi found an ingenious way to solve this dilemma. At this time the language of the Sumerians was dying out in Mesopotamia, and, to preserve the old Sumerian legends, they were being translated into the Akkadian language, which was chiefly used for literature and diplomacy. He saw to it that, in the translation, Marduk, the god of Babylon, was given a special status. In this new version it was related that, in return for important service, he had been elected king of all the gods. In this way he received divine authority for his preeminent position and became an important influence in unifying the Babylonian civilization.

One of Hammurabi's great achievements was the establishment of a code of law for the government of his empire. There had been earlier local law codes as far back as the 24th century B.C. based largely on tradition or custom, designed to serve peace and justice and the satisfaction of the city god. Hammurabi's code had far wider application, applying to an empire. Its basic purpose was stated in the introduction: "When Marduk commanded me to give justice to the people of the land, and to let them have good governance, I set forth truth and justice to the people of the land and prospered the people."

One of the chief responsibilities of the state was the maintenance of canals and farmlands which were the foundation of the common welfare. The farmer, who generally worked the land under a yearly contract with its owner, was subject to a detailed system of penalties for failure to maintain the land in good condition or to handle it properly. Every holder of land was responsible for maintaining the bank of any canal that flowed past his fields. Especially heavy penalties were assessed if his failure to do so caused loss to other users of the canal.

After the death of Hammurabi in 1749 B.C., a series of invasions and revolts divided the empire, slowly cutting the trade routes which brought in timber, metals, and other important supplies. In the 16th century B.C. the Hittites, from beyond the Taurus Mountains, speaking an Indo-European language, attacked and plundered Babylon. Other invaders during the same century brought in the deadly horse-drawn chariot, a new weapon which was almost irresistible on the battlefield.

With constant warfare, farmlands and canals were neglected, food production dwindled, and several of the ancient cities were deserted. Toward the end of the fifteenth century B.C., Egypt, seeking to extend its power into Mesopotamia, and in search of allies, supplied gold to help with the restoration of Babylon and nearby cities, including Nippur, but as the years went by this supply dried up. The next 1,300 years saw a continuing struggle between Babylon, Egypt, Assyria, and other powers for mastery in Mesopotamia. During these years Babylon was captured no less than twelve times and more than once reduced to ruins. There were times of famine or siege when people were reduced to eating human flesh.

Finally, in 689 B.C., the Assyrian king Sennacherib stormed Babylon and attempted to wipe it out. Buildings and defenses were pulled down and burned, and the bank of the Euphrates River was altered to divert water onto the land, turning the whole area into a swamp. The city had ceased to exist, but the countryside still needed administration. The loss of the city had done nothing to lessen the opposition of the Babylonian people. Reconciliation seemed the best policy. Sennacherib's son married a Babylonian wife and adopted the worship of Marduk and other Babylonian gods, and in 680 B.C. he set out to rebuild the city on a grander scale than before. Within thirty years another Assyrian king returned to besiege the city. By the time it was captured the streets were piled with corpses and the starving survivors were eating human flesh. The Babylonian king set his palace on fire and died in the flames.

Now the tables slowly turned. The Medes, who had been building their numbers in Mesopotamia, joined with Babylon and began advancing into Assyrian territory. In 614 B.C. the Medes destroyed the Assyrian city of Assur together with its inhabitants. Two years later the Medes combined with Babylon to besiege and burn the Assyrian capital of Nineveh. In 607 B.C. the Egyptian Pharaoh Necho gathered his full army to protect his interests in Syria, but in 605 the Babylonian crown prince, Nebuchadnezzar, surprised him at Carchemish and annihilated the Egyptian Army. In 539 B.C. the Persian King, Cyrus of Anshan, with bribery and subversion, persuaded many of the local priests and princes to join him in overcoming the tyranny of Babylon. When he entered the city he was welcomed as a liberator. However, the Persian rule was oppressive and corrupt, and the land was ready to welcome Alexander the Great when he defeated the Persian Army and entered Babylon in 331 B.C.

Alexander continued his victorious way eastward to India and Bactria. He dreamt of plans for a sea route to Egypt and India. Returning to Babylon he started on a project for an enormous harbor and several dockyards for the building of a fleet. Babylon faced the prospect of again becoming one of the great cities of the world until, in 323 B.C., Alexander died of a fever.

The death of Alexander was followed by years of nearly continuous fighting for power among rival claimants until, by 309 B.C., Seleucus, one of Alexander's officers, had gained control. He faced the Herculean task of rebuilding the city from an enormous mass of rubble left by the fighting. He also shared Alexander's vision of a sea route to India. For this purpose the Tigris would be a better river than the Euphrates. He decided to build a new city, Seleuceia, on the Tigris, about forty miles north of Babylon, and he went on to extend his empire as far as India. Babylon had sunk to a depopulated ruin.

Here was a city with fortifications that appeared impregnable. Within the walls were the temples of Marduk, Ninmah, Ishtar, and other gods, the great tower of Babel, 300 feet square at its base and nearly 300 feet high, the royal palace, with its fortified citadel, and the Hanging Gardens, celebrated as one of the seven wonders of the ancient world. Within the sacred precinct of Marduk was his shrine room, 130 feet long by 66 feet wide, the walls and roof beams plated with gold and precious stones. Herodotus mentions the gold altar, throne, and statues of the god, with a total weight, he was told, of more than eighteen tons. Beside this shrine were the chapels of other deities.

This tremendous work of construction tells of progress in the arts, science, and mathematics, the last of which used a system of roots and powers and decimals, a system superior to any other in the ancient world.

Through these centuries of change and development there were many changes in the world around Babylon. The forests were being cut on the upland hillsides for the making of buildings, for the baking of bricks, for the building of boats, and for shipment to Egypt which lacked timber. In the high country away from the fertile land of the great river valleys, tribes of nomadic herdsmen lived by raising sheep and goats. As they increased in numbers, beyond the carrying capacity of their grazing lands, they had to either destroy their grasslands through overgrazing or spread outward to find new pasture. This they did on a huge scale, moving back and forth over the face of southern Asia, often bringing their flocks to land already overgrazed by other occupants.

Sheep and goats can destroy the protecting grass cover on a hillside as effectively as a swarm of locusts. A look at the ruined lands in the American Southwest—the silted rivers and reservoirs—can give a graphic picture of the causes that lay behind the silting of the irrigation canals of Mesopotamia and of the pressures that drove the tides of nomadic invaders into Mesopotamia. Modern methods can partly repair the damage caused by misuse of land and, through wise use, can avoid further damage. But this requires organized discipline and motivation among the users of the land. This was lacking in the turbulent environment of Mesopotamia. The dawning of civilization had changed a small population that could live successfully off the land, into a greater population that was forced to overuse it and destroy its carrying capacity, fighting savagely in the process for ownership of what was left.

In the space of a hundred centuries man had come out from his early caves, learned how to make the earth productive, left step by step records of his rise in the understanding and mastery of his environment and in the creation of beauty and splendor. He had built the first civilization of history and then, through his multiplication and his instinct for aggression and personal dominance, he had pulled this great edifice apart, piece by piece, while at the same time he destroyed the foundation of natural resources on which the whole structure was built.

Out of this welter of obsolete instincts a few great leaders had arisen to build empires of disciplined peace and prosperity, empires that lasted only so long as the personal fire of the leader survived. Other civilizations, starting shortly after, were going through rather similar cycles of growth, experience, and decay—in Egypt, India, and China. Other leaders were promoting ideas which, as they spread, could discipline the human emotions more lastingly and effectively than those of generals and princes. Moses, in the 13th century B.C., brought down from the mountain the Ten Commandments given him by a single, all-powerful God. In India in the 6th century B.C., Prince Siddhartha Gautama, later known as the Buddha, preached a way of life that included in essence the spirit of the Ten Commandments. These two, followed a little later by Christ and Mohammed, spread ideas which have had more effect on human history than the greatest kings and generals.

Throughout the early attempts at civilization we see man searching for a solution to the paradox of human nature. Gifted with intelligence and reason, he finds these powers nullified by an instinctive driving force that is stronger than reason. To this day the search continues for some effective basis for a civilizing motivation that can be built into human culture and carried forward from generation to generation. Here lies the key to the search for civilization.

CHAPTER V

Science and the Population Explosion

With the growth of settled communities the crowding centers of population began to face one of the major enforcing agencies of natural law. Through the centuries the slow accumulation of filth in the cities built up a health problem. Refuse and excrement piled up in the streets or at the city outskirts, where unwanted babies were also left to die. The level of the streets was slowly raised as this accumulated filth built up. Except at the early palaces, no effort appears to have been made for cleanliness and sanitation. The growing cities began to smother under their accumulating filth, and now nature's next line of defense, pestilence, began to take over.

In the 5th century B.C. Thucydides described the symptoms of cholera in Athens. In the same century, Hippocrates described malaria. These are two of the oldest and most destructive recorded epidemic diseases of man and may have been with him long before these early records. Bubonic plague was described by Rufus of Ephesus in the 1st century A.D. In the 5th century A.D. there was a fifty-year cycle of epidemics covering the Roman world. In 8th-century

England there was a series of four epidemics of bubonic plague. After that, for some reason, epidemics of the plague in Europe were infrequent until the 14th century. Then, in December, 1347, it appeared in some of the ports of Italy, apparently brought in by ships from Black Sea ports. By the following June it had spread northward, covering all of Italy, eastern Spain, France, southern Hungary, and the western shore of the Adriatic. It moved slowly northward, striking hardest in the crowded towns, especially in the summer when the carrier fleas were perhaps most active. By December, 1348, it had reached southern England. The following June it included most of England, the southeast coast of Ireland, most of Hungary, and the Holy Roman Empire. By December, 1349, the plague had spread through all of England, most of Ireland and Scotland, Denmark, southern Norway, and Poland. By December, 1350, it covered most of Norway and Sweden.

There are few adequate data for this period, but it has been estimated by demographers that, during the years of the epidemic, the population of Europe dropped from roughly 84 million to about 60 million. This crisis was followed by a series of outbreaks in Europe, coming approximately every ten years. London had at least twenty attacks of the plague during the 15th century; it struck Venice 23 times between 1348 and 1576. But, in spite of these outbreaks, Europe's population continued to rise, reaching 110 million in the 17th century, when another severe outbreak reduced the numbers by 10 million. Among individual cities, Florence lost half its population of 90,000, and Hamburg apparently lost almost two thirds of its inhabitants. In 1720 Marseilles lost 40,000 out of 90,000 inhabitants, while Vienna suffered 76,000 plague deaths in 1679, and Prague had 83,000 casualties in 1681.

We can imagine the conditions that led up to, and later flowed from, such epidemics. Lewis Mumford quotes the archaeologist Rodolfo Lanciani who commented on the sanitary conditions of early Rome, with its huge population, in time of plague. Lanciani excavated some of the burial pits used during the epidemics. Groups of these pits, each twelve feet square by thirty feet deep, were filled with corpses thrown in as if they were carrion till the street level was reached. When the pits were filled the corpses were thrown into the moat beside the wall of Servius Tullius—all this in addition to sewage from the heavily populated city. During the recent excavations the workmen had to be relieved from time to time, overcome by the unbearable stench still remaining after a lapse of two thousand years.

It is no wonder that many altars and shrines were dedicated to the Goddess of Fever, or that Rome experienced a series of devastating plagues between 23 B.C. and 162 A.D.

We have seen the figures for the losses from the plague in a few cities. Add to these disasters the losses from cholera, malaria, smallpox, typhus, typhoid fever, and tuberculosis throughout Europe, China, India, and other parts of Asia, and we can perhaps now conceive of the effectiveness of these biological controls in keeping the growth of the world's population within bounds.

The "black death" increased the widespread belief in witchcraft. John Calvin was convinced that a group of witches, acting as agents of Satan, brought the plague to Geneva. Jews and witches were hunted down in the streets as the originators of the plague. Some physicians were stoned in the streets of France as spreaders of the plague.

In spite of the huge losses, the human birth rate still exceeded the death rate. The population increased, rather slowly, until, in the 19th century, two world-shaking breakthroughs took place. The Industrial Revolution, with the use of steam power, and, later, electricity, vastly increased man's ability to provide for his physical wants and to support large city populations. At almost the same time, another series of discoveries began to lift the controls that had regulated the pace of human expansion. Between 1775 and 1796, Edward Jenner was at work on experiments to show that smallpox could be controlled by the use of a vaccine. In 1803, a large-scale test was undertaken: 12,000 persons were vaccinated in London, and the average annual death rate dropped from 2,018 to 622.

In 1848 Louis Pasteur discovered that bacteria caused fermentation in beer and milk, and mankind gained the knowledge that bacteria lay at the root of many human health problems. This led to the development of antiseptic surgery and more general use of antiseptics about 1865. Meanwhile, Florence Nightingale, against violent opposition, was able, during the Crimean War, to effect reforms in the management of hospital sanitation. In the months from February to June, 1855, the death rate in the British hospitals in the Crimea dropped from 42% to 2%. Robert Koch isolated the bacillus of tuberculosis in 1882 and the cholera bacillus in 1883. These discoveries opened the way for effective world campaigns against disease and tremendous reductions in the world death rate. But the fight was still slow and uncertain.

Finally, in 1938, Alexander Fleming discovered penicillin and created for medicine a whole new dimension in the fight against disease. During World War II the development of DDT presented another spectacular field for action. This, along with other potent new poisons, drastically changed man's environment; through the ability to control insects and other disease carriers it became a new lifesaving weapon against disease. It was particularly effective against the malaria-carrying mosquito, one of man's worst killers. With the advent of DDT, Ceylon, one of the countries hardest hit by malaria, reduced its death rate by 75% in ten years.

Thus, within a very short space of time, by great forward leaps, man increased his ability to combat the controlling forces of nature, to survive the vicissitudes of life, and to lengthen the span of his life on earth. In India, for example, the average life expectancy at birth rose from twenty years in 1930 to forty-two years in 1961. In the United States it increased from 47 years in 1900 to about 70 years in 1960. In other countries throughout the world there have been comparable increases.

At first these increases were hailed as great advances for the human race, but as their effects began to build up it became apparent that they also pose one of the greatest dangers that man has ever faced. With the lowering of the human death rate, while the birth rate remained little changed, there appeared a serious imbalance between the amount of incoming new life and the outgoing old life on the planet. Man had broken a basic natural law; his population began to multiply out of control; the "population explosion" had started.

Section II

TODAY

CHAPTER VI

Population and Carrying Capacity

The phrase "population explosion" has perhaps been overused, and it may have lost some of its impact but it is a convenient and not inaccurate description of what is taking place in the world today. It is an explosion that holds as much danger for the human race as does the hydrogen bomb, for human reproduction is sparked by its own automatic energizer. The bomb may hopefully be kept under control if the pressures of human overcrowding can first be mastered. These pressures today are expanding out of control.

It took the human race nearly two million years to attain a population of one billion people by the early nineteenth century. The second billion, by contrast, was achieved in about a hundred years in the early 1930's, and the third billion was added in only thirty years, by the 1960's. At the present rate of reproduction the three billion will double to become six billion in about forty years. At this rate the physical limits of the world's carrying capacity come clearly into sight.

While some politicians and scientists talk bravely about the coming ability to feed the growing masses on algae, yeast, and synthetic foods, it is obvious that food, for all its importance, is only one of many related problems. Among the most important of these is the quality of life and the ability of human nature within man to tolerate the crowding numbers of his fellow men, with the rights and needs of each individual competing with those of his neighbor. The quality of life with its growing tensions sets a limit to the world's carrying capacity just as surely as does the food supply; for, as the food supply shrinks, the tensions of competition for that food must multiply.

This chart will help to recall Chapter I and the bacteria which, uncontrolled and doubling their number every half hour, would equal the bulk of the earth in less than a week. At first this multiplication was invisible to the eye, but as the multiplying population increased into an explosion, three

Projected Population Growth*

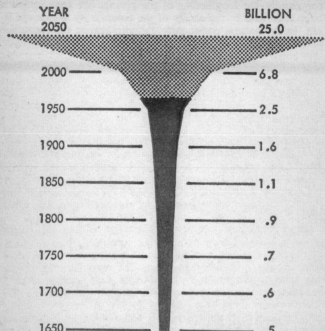

YEAR	BILLION
2050	25.0
2000	6.8
1950	2.5
1900	1.6
1850	1.1
1800	.9
1750	.7
1700	.6
1650	.5

* Population Reference Bureau—reprinted by permission.

quarters of the entire bulk of the earth appeared during the last hour. Starting the hour with a quarter of the bulk, it doubled to a half, then again to the full size, overflowing.

The world population today is already reaching its own "last hour." The most optimistic estimate of the number that could be fed by modern science is 50 billion. At the present rate of growth that number will be reached in the twenty-first century; but, long before that, the question will arise of how many can live together without committing mass suicide. It seems clear that environmental resistance will act to slow the growth rate, perhaps by poisoning the air, the water, and the soil with the waste products of civilization. The changing environment may reduce man's desire to procreate. The world statesmen and religious leaders may find ways to control the tide, or human nature may take control through hatreds and aggression.

Entirely aside from the question of total numbers in the community, the lengthening of the average life span makes a huge difference in the ability of the community to manage itself. In the natural community, fighting against the resistance of the environment, few members lived past the age when they could provide for their own maintenance. Each member was, on the average, a producing asset, contributing to the welfare of the whole.

Today's startling increase in population comes both in the greater number of dependent elderly people, incapable of supporting themselves, and, especially, in the proportion of children who live beyond infancy. The added burden of their support falls on the members of producing age. It has been estimated from the census bureau reports that in 1940 there were in the United States 71 people in the dependent age group (under 20 or over 64) for every 100 of producing age (20 to 64) and that, at the present indicated growth rate, this proportion will have risen to 104 dependents, largely children, for each 100 producers by 1980.

The United States and other developed nations are taxing their citizens to pour billions of dollars into helping the hungry nations to increase their food production and become self-supporting. Some of them, even with this help, are losing ground in the race with the flood of new mouths, so that their food production per capita has actually decreased.

In 1950 North America had about 168 million people, while Latin America had about 163 million. By the year 2000, at their present growth rates, North America will have about 388 million, while Latin America will have shot ahead to about 756 million. Asia, during the same time, will have jumped from 1,380 million up to 4,401 million.

Until the time of the Second World War all the major regions of the world were raising enough food for their own needs. By 1961 all except North America, the U.S.S.R., and Oceania were depending on imported grain that totaled 45 million metric tons to meet their food deficits. By 1963 only North America and Oceania were net exporters. In the face of this growing need the available area of arable land in the world was declining. The United States, for example, is losing more than a million acres a year to highways, airports, houses, erosion, and other causes.

If we assume that it might be possible for the world to avoid nuclear war or other catastrophes under these growing pressures, we might consider the island of Mauritius for a preview of the future. This island in the Indian Ocean was uninhabited until the 17th century. The first permanent settle-

ment was established by the French in 1721. Sugar and cotton were planted, and large numbers of slaves were imported
to work the sugar fields. The British took over the island in
1810, and by 1833 the population had reached 100,000, including about 75,000 slaves. Later many more workers were
brought in from India, and many Chinese immigrated to the
island.

In the early years the island was known for its healthful
climate, but the growing population brought growing problems of sanitation. Ships brought rats and the plague and
other diseases, and during the 19th and 20th centuries the island was swept by epidemics of smallpox, cholera, bubonic
plague, and influenza. After 1862, malaria became a serious
problem, finally emerging as the island's chief killer.

During the first 15 years of the 20th century the deaths actually exceeded births. But a great revolution in health came
during the Second World War, with the introduction of
DDT. The death loss from malaria dropped from 3,534 in
1945 (nearly a quarter of all deaths) to only 3 in 1955.
Meanwhile, with an improvement in sanitary conditions, the
infant mortality changed. Between 1944 and 1948, 155 babies in every 1,000 died during their first year of life. By 1961
the rate had dropped to 62 deaths per thousand. With these
changes the average life expectancy at birth rose from 33
years to 60 years by 1961. But this happy increase brought
with it great problems.

By 1962, 47% of the population was reported to be in the
dependent age group (under 15 or over 65). Meanwhile the
producing half of the population was finding it steadily more
difficult to provide the needed food and supplies. A large proportion of these had to be imported, and to pay for them the
island depended on its one major crop, sugar. But the population had grown past the carrying capacity of the island. It
could no longer produce enough sugar to pay for the needed
imports. The per capita income had actually declined. A high
proportion of the people were suffering from malnutrition
and anemia. The number of men receiving government assistance increased sixfold between 1953 and 1959.

Valiant attempts have been made by the government to improve the island's economy and educational system, but living
conditions have become almost intolerable in some areas. The
island already has one of the world's heaviest population den-
sities: 888 per square mile; yet, at its present rate of growth,
this population will double in just 23 years.

Richard L. Meier, Research Associate at the School of
Natural Resources, University of Michigan, after a study,

predicted that, as the indigent population continues to increase, the growing pressures could lead to martial law and the establishment of government camps to care for the growing numbers of unemployed. The problems of maintaining order under these conditions could lead to a public demand that the camps be enclosed by barbed wire—a sort of prison where the inmates would discover that they really had been born to serve life terms.

In the early 1950's, the governor appointed a committee to study the situation. With half its membership made up of Roman Catholics, this committee recommended, in a report published in 1955, that "the Government should without delay . . . initiate and promote within the framework of the Social Services the proper organizations capable of assisting the population by advice on and practical aid in family planning methods. . . ."

Mauritius is only a small piece of land in the Indian Ocean, where it is very easy to see the clear limits to its possibilities for growth, and the tragic results when those limits are reached. The world is a huge place and it is perhaps hard to visualize the limits to its carrying capacity. But those limits are there. They too are definite, and for the first time in human history they are coming clearly into sight where they can be measured in years, unless the world finds a cure for the condition. The late Dr. Alan Gregg, who headed the medical work of the Rockefeller Institute, raised the question whether the population explosion would eventually generate forces that would control or cure itself, or whether the population growth had gone beyond the self-limiting stage and become a sort of malignancy on the body of mankind that must become fatal if he cannot discover a cure.

Our demographers can predict how the populations will grow if the present rates continue unchecked, but what can we say about the forces that may change these rates? For a single example, we know that with the huge plantings of food crops that are necessary to sustain the world's population, and with the wide commerce in foods of many kinds, the spreading of insect pests has faced mankind with the choice of controlling the insects or starving. In many cases the most effective control has been by means of the modern pesticides: DDT and many others. Some of these have produced wholly unexpected side effects. Studies have shown that DDT can be fed to pheasants and quail in amounts so small that they cause no apparent physical harm, but they do gradually accumulate in the body and, among other harmful effects, can cause sterility; or, if any young are produced, they are weak and in their turn are unsuccessful parents. This kind of effect need not come from the direct feeding of the birds. Earthworms may take in DDT that falls from sprayed trees and store the poison in their bodies through the winter. When they are eaten by robins the following spring they can poison the robins and so wipe out a community of robins. This actually happened at the campus of the Michigan State University.

DDT washing off a sprayed area into a lake or stream may be taken up by the microscopic plankton in the water and thus infect the fish that eat them. The fish, in turn, have been shown to poison the grebes and other birds that eat them. Fish taken in the ocean many miles from the nearest land have been found carrying large amounts of DDT. The bald eagle lives largely on fish; it has dropped off alarmingly in numbers in the past few years. The National Audubon Society has carried on a nationwide study on problems of its reproduction. Many nests have been found with eggs that failed to hatch. Some of these eggs contained DDT. This would seem to suggest that if the spreading of the poison continues, humans, as well, will eat fish at their peril.

No one yet knows what effect this spreading of the new pesticides may eventually have on the reproductive capacities of the human race. The late Rachel Carson has given a vivid picture of some of the problems in her best-selling book, *Silent Spring*. A great deal of research work is now being done on the problem by the government, and answers may be found that will refute some of the forecasts, but here we see one of the little-understood factors that may bear on the problem.

Another factor is crowding. In a study conducted through the cooperation of the National Institute of Mental Health at Bethesda, Maryland, and the Jackson Memorial Laboratory at Bar Harbor, Maine, it was shown that crowding beyond certain limits produced both physical and psychological disturbances in laboratory mice. This was made evident through increased physical activity and fighting among the males and, in the females, by lower rates of reproduction and by destruction or eating of the young that were born. There was a considerable difference between two different strains of mice in their ability to adjust to the stresses of crowded conditions and in the level of crowding they could tolerate without bad results.

In summing up his report on this study, Mr. John B. Calhoun of the National Institute of Mental Health stated: "We have seen that a fairly physiologically and behaviorally stable animal . . . can be altered into an unstable one merely by increasing the size of the group. A look at some of our human problems of social unrest, juvenile delinquency and political upheaval, suggests very strongly that man is not immune to some of the same social pressures as mice."

The rapid growth of world tensions suggests that long before the world reaches the limits of its potential food supply it may reach the limits of man's tolerance for his fellowman, or, perhaps we should say, his tolerance for the environment that is being built by himself and his crowding fellows. What are the positive steps that he can take to bring his reproductive rate more nearly into balance with the necessities imposed by natural law? Barring some unforeseen catastrophe the world's death rate can be expected to continue its decline. The best hope then, for avoiding certain eventual catastrophe, must lie in finding some way to control the world's birth rate.

There is still a great deal that is not known about the mental, emotional, and physical influence that affect a nation's birth rate. Millions of dollars are being spent by government and private organizations, but far more is needed. The federal government has taken some very encouraging steps to spread information and help where it is needed, and the nation appears to have become aware of the situation. The birth rate in the United States, after a long uptrend starting in 1939, started down in 1957.

In 1961, with the introduction of the "pill" and, later, with the development of new contraceptive techniques, there came a much steeper decline in the birth rate. Surveys have indicated that nearly 90% of U.S. women of childbearing age now practice birth control in some form. In addition it has been estimated that there are at least a million illegal abortions in the nation each year. (This figure, at best only an educated guess, appeared to be the consensus of competent witnesses before Senator Gruening's Subcommittee on Foreign Aid Expenditures. See *Population Bulletin XXII*, #5, December 1966.)

It is noteworthy that, although the rise in the U.S. birth rate had been higher among the nonwhite women than among the white, when the decline started, it also was steeper among the nonwhite women, especially among those with an education. It is important to remember that, in spite of the declining birth rate (based on the number of children per 1,000 women of childbearing age), the actual number of births is likely to keep on rising as the huge new group of youngsters reach maturity. For example, in 1930 there were eleven million women of the peak childbearing age between twenty and twenty-nine years. By 1960 there were still only

eleven million; but by 1970 the oncoming young will have
raised the number to fifteen million, and by 1980 this will
grow to twenty million. Even with a falling birth rate, however, it is estimated that between the years 2000 and 2010
the U.S. population will grow by 75 million, nearly double
the increase of the decade forty years earlier.

All of the industrialized nations now have the means to
control their population growth. The real problem lies with
the underdeveloped hungry nations that are threatened with
starvation and chaos. With *them,* efforts at control are hampered by custom, taboo, illiteracy, ignorance, and the great
expense of bringing understanding and motivation to widely
scattered populations. Japan, a highly developed country, has
showed that it can be done. She cut her birth rate in half in
just twelve years, from 1947 to 1959. This started with the
passage of the Eugenic Protection Law of 1948 which legalized abortion. In 1955 there were 1,170,000 legal abortions
in Japan. A survey in 1957 showed that 57% of Japanese
families practiced contraception in some form, chiefly for
economic reasons or for the health of the mother.

The story has been very different in some of the less developed countries where, as in India, some parts of the country
would actually be facing famine without millions of tons of
grain in aid from the United States and smaller gifts from
other nations. The problem of organizing, training, and transporting the army of birth control workers to a nation of 470
million people speaking about 170 different languages and dialects can hardly be imagined.

It has been pointed out as significant that in the Indian
state of Madras, where 80% of the villages have electricity,
the birth rate is about half that of the nation as a whole
where, in the dark villages, the only recreation at night is
procreation. This might have far-reaching implications for
many problem areas. Puerto Rico, a nation with only a small
fraction of the problems of India, has carried out a fairly
successful program of control despite the determined opposition of her Roman Catholic hierarchy. Egypt, Pakistan, and a
number of other countries are carrying out organized programs of family planning, and the problems are enormous
and will require massive, organized, and many-sided help
from the more developed countries.

The community of living things might usefully be compared to the human body, in which each microscopic cell
shares in the experience of growth, function, decay, discard,
and replacement. Within this body there is a system which
automatically limits the replacement of worn-out cells to the

WORLD POPULATION DATA MID-1964   *From Population Reference Bureau*   *Continental Population Estimates*
(Reprinted by Permission)

Key to Growth	
Rate of Increase %	Years Required to Double
0.5%	139 yr.
1.0	70 "
1.5	47 "
2.0	35 "
2.5	28 "
3.0	23 "
3.5	20 "
4.0	18 "

	Mid-1964	1980 Projection, Provisional U.N. Estimate	Literacy* over 15 yrs.
Africa	303 million	449 million	5–10%
Asia	1,843 "	2,404 "	10–15 "
N. America	211 "	267 "	10–15 "
Latin America	236 "	374 "	35–40 "
Europe	443 "	479 "	20–25 "
Oceania	18 "	23 "	15–20 "
U.S.S.R.	229 "	278 "	70–75 "
World Total	3,283 million	4,274 million	

Selected Countries	Population	Growth Rate	1980 Projection
Morocco	13.1 million	3.0%	22.4 million
Sudan	13.2 "	2.8 "	19.3 "
U.A.R. (Egypt)	28.7 "	2.6 "	46.8 "
Nigeria	56.0 "		91.0 "
Iran	22.6 "	1.9 "	33.1 "
Turkey	30.8 "	2.6 "	48.5 "
India	468.5 "	2.3 "	661.5 "
Pakistan	100.7 "	2.1 "	153.6 "
Indonesia	102.2 "	2.2 "	152.8 "
Philippines	31.2 "	3.2 "	55.8 "
Thailand	29.7 "	3.0 "	47.5 "
South Vietnam	15.9 "	3.7 "	21.9 "
China—Mainland	690.0 "	2.1 "	840.0 "

Selected Countries	Population	Growth Rate	1980 Projection	Literacy* over 15 yrs.
China—Taiwan	12.1 million	3.6 %	17.2 million	50–55%
Japan	96.8 "	0.9 "	111.1 "	98–99 "
Costa Rica	1.4 "	4.3 "	2.4 "	
Dominican Republic	3.5 "	3.6 "	6.2 "	75–80 "
El Salvador	2.8 "	3.6 "	4.6 "	
Guatemala	4.2 "	3.2 "	6.9 "	
Honduras	2.1 "	3.0 "	3.7 "	
Mexico	39.6 "	3.1 "	70.8 "	65–70 "
Nicaragua	1.6 "	3.5 "	2.8 "	
Panama	1.2 "	3.3 "	2.0 "	
Puerto Rico	2.6 "	1.7 "	3.1 "	
Argentina	21.7 "	1.6 "	29.0 "	30–35 "
Brazil	79.8 "	3.0 "	123.7 "	45–50 "
Ecuador	4.8 "	3.2 "	8.0 "	
Peru	11.9 "	3.0 "	17.5 "	
Venezuela	8.4 "	3.4 "	14.9 "	50–55 "
U.S.	192.1 "	1.6 "	240.9 "	98–99 "
Belgium	9.3 "	0.5 "	10.1 "	
France	48.4 "	1.2 "	53.3 "	
Netherlands	12.1 "	1.3 "	14.1 "	96–97 "
United Kingdom	54.1 "	0.8 "	57.3 "	
Czechoslovakia	14.0 "	0.7 "	15.8 "	98–99 "
West Germany**	56.2 "	1.3 "	58.5 "	
Hungary	10.1 "	0.4 "	10.7 "	98–99 "
Poland	31.1 "	1.3 "	38.0 "	
Italy	50.8 "	0.6 "	56.4 "	85–90 "
Romania	19.0 "	0.9 "	22.3 "	
Spain	31.3 "	0.8 "	36.0 "	85–90 "

* 1963 figures

** Not including West Berlin

number that will maintain for each part of the body its proper size and function. If this controlling system fails to function properly, the healthy cell growth turns to malignancy that will poison and destroy the entire body if it is not checked.

Today, man has destroyed important parts of the natural control system which formerly regulated the numbers in the body of the human community. The resulting growth is taking on the character of an uncontrolled malignancy. A cure may still be possible if mankind can agree to take the necessary steps, but time is short and agreement on their use is slow in coming.

In the following chapters we shall try to assess some of the symptoms of the disease, some of the steps that are being undertaken to cure it, and the problems that they face.

CHAPTER VII

Food

We have seen the growing number of mouths that the world will be called upon to feed. The urgency of this problem becomes clear as we realize that nearly half of the world's population today is suffering from malnutrition. Undernourishment handicaps the development of children from the start, leading to irreversible damage, with a high incidence of physical and mental retardation. The adults are perpetually tired, with their productive ability far below par, poorly equipped to build a self-sustaining community. We know that, as things are going, the world's need for food will more than double within the short space of forty years. What chances does humanity have to meet and survive this crisis? What assets does it have to draw on?

The first great asset, of course, is productive land. The land area of the globe reaches a total of 32.9 billion acres; of this, only 3.5 billion, or 11%, is classified as arable or used for tree crops; besides this, there are 6.352 billion acres classified as meadow or permanent pasture, leaving 23.071 billion acres covered by desert, mountain, or the works of man—or other surface that is not favorable for the production of food. Thus we see roughly 30% of the earth's land surface that is readily adapted to produce food, while the remaining 70% is mostly unsuitable.

Of this latter 70%, there is still a considerable amount that could be cultivated if man can solve such problems as local weather, water supply, soil quality, or other hazards. For example, Russia has had huge areas of unused fertile soil which were plowed and planted in a recent costly major effort; but so far the project seems to have been unsuccessful due to unfavorable climatic conditions, among other problems.

There are many millions of unused acres in the world that will no doubt be made productive some day as man learns to overcome the special problems that they present; but this may be a very costly and time-consuming undertaking. There is the further problem that the good land is rather unevenly divided, with the developed countries having the larger share of good land per capita.

The regional shares are estimated (on page 63) in millions of acres.

There is a tremendous variation in the distribution of arable land among the different countries. In Europe, for example, Denmark is blessed by having 65% of her total land area classified as arable, while Norway has only 2–3%. India has 49% so classified, while China has only 11%. Latin America has only 5%. Australia and Canada, two leading food producers, cultivate only 3–4%.

Among the arable regions, there are great variations in the kinds and the amounts of food that can be produced. These are determined largely by such factors as the climate, quality of the soil, and availability of water, which may have to be carried for long distances from its source by canals.

Rice, for example, requires wet land, where corn would not grow. Wheat, in turn, requires conditions that would be too dry for rice. A cold climate with a short growing season might prevent the growing of all three, but might permit the growing of such hardy crops as cabbage or kale. Religion might prevent the growing of beef for food, as in India.

Man's principal sources of food energy were estimated for 1958 as follows:

Rice	21.2%
Wheat	19.6
Corn	5.4
Potatoes	4.9
All others	48.9

Geographic Region	Arable & Tree Crops Area	%	Permanent Meadow & Pasture	%	All Other	Total Area	%
N. America	566	16.3	688	10.8	3,524	4,778	14.5
Latin America	252	7.2	913	14.4	3,902	5,067	15.4
West Europe	242	7.0	140	2.2	522	904	2.8
U.S.S.R. & East Europe	686	19.8	967	15.2	4,198	5,851	17.8
Africa	583	16.8	1,463	23.0	5,429	7,475	22.7
Asia	1,073	30.9	1,077	17.0	4,559	6,709	20.4
Oceania	69	2.0	1,104	17.4	937	2,110	6.4
World total excluding Greenland and Antarctica	3,471	100.0	6,352	100.0	23,071	32,894	100.0

Economic Regions	Arable & Tree Crops Area	%	Permanent Meadow & Pasture	%	All Other	Total Area	%
Developed	1,563	45	2,899	45.6	6,181	13,643	41.5
Less Developed	1,908	55	3,453	54.4	13,890	19,251	58.5

Political Regions	Arable & Tree Crops Area	%	Permanent Meadow & Pasture	%	All Other	Total Area	%
Free World	2,515	72.5	4,946	77.9	17,170	24,631	74.9
Communist	956	27.5	1,406	22.1	5,901	8,263	25.1

Clearly grain is the principal source of calories. There is a big difference in the food values of various grains. Rice is a more effective producer of food energy than wheat, with an average yield of 1.8 million calories to the acre, nearly double that of the 0.96 million calories produced by wheat. Thus, in spite of the much greater acreage of wheat that is planted, 506 million acres against only 290 million, rice still stands as the major producer of energy.

Calories, for all their importance, tell only a part of the story. Protein deficiency causes kwashiorkor, the most widespread single disease in the hungry countries. It may cause irreparable damage to the growing child, harming the liver, pancreas, and skin and impairing certain body functions.

Most plant foods, including the grains, are poor in protein content, and what they do carry is of a quality that, by itself, cannot be most effectively used by the body. However, fish or other animal products can supply the missing amino acids which enable the body to synthesize the vegetable proteins. Meal from some of the oilseeds, such as cottonseed, soybeans, and peanuts also supply missing ingredients to make the vegetable proteins more effective. With this knowledge, nutritionists have been able to transform a deficient diet into an adequate one through inexpensive mixtures of foods. These have proved very valuable in lands with deficient food supplies.

Many diets suffer through the lack of other ingredients than protein. Goiter, which was once a scourge in many parts of the world, has been conquered simply by the addition of iodine to the salt in the diet. Diets of polished rice or refined wheat flour have lost much of their vitamin B content in the processing. It is now general practice to enrich such refined flour with the missing niacin, riboflavin, and thiamin in the United States and Canada. This is required by law in Puerto Rico and some Latin American countries. Many common food plants contain harmful chemicals, which are made harmless by cooking or other processing. Cabbage contains chemicals that impede the use of essential iodine by the thyroid gland. Soybeans and other legumes contain a material that interferes with the digestion of protein. Other plants carry materials which interfere with the use of calcium and iron by the body, and so on. From this it becomes clear that any diet which lacks sufficient variety can be dangerous if not processed and eaten with proper understanding.

So much for the food-producing areas and the crops that produce the food. Knowing that more than half the world is suffering from food deficiency today and that within a very few years the food requirements of the world will be doubled, are there any steps that can be taken to meet the multiplying demand? Yes, there are still some rather limited areas of potentially productive land that can be brought into bearing without much expense. There are also other areas that can be made productive through major undertakings by government or cooperative effort, such as the coordinated management of an entire watershed, with reservoirs and the digging of canals and irrigation systems to store and distribute the water. Finally, there are areas where the land is fully utilized, but which can be made more productive through more effective management. For example, Japan produces, on the average, 4,000 pounds of rice to the acre, while India averages not much over 1,000 pounds. In recent years the United States has produced an average of 56 bushels of corn per acre while Mexico has produced 14.

The pace of improvement can be shown by a few simple steps: In 1910 it took nearly 2¼ acres in the United States to feed one person for a year, but by 1962 farm productivity had so increased that it took just under 1¼ acres to do the same job. At the same time the number of people who could be fed through the labor of one farm worker rose from roughly 11 in 1940 to 28, with some surplus left over, in 1962.

We might ask how this was accomplished and how some of the hungry nations might hope to achieve the same kind of result. There is no simple answer. The progress in the United States came as the result of many forward steps in many different fields.

Perhaps the most obvious step lay in maintaining or improving the quality of the soil—using more fertilizer to replace the minerals drawn from the soil by earlier crops and adding fertilizer and humus to build up poor or worn-out soil. A lot has been learned about the proper use of fertilizer, to meet the specific needs of different soils. A fertilizer mixture that will improve one soil may hurt another that has a different mineral composition. Too much nitrogen, for example, may not only hurt the nutritive quality of the crop, but may make the plants more subject to damage by wind or rain. Machinery, too, has helped enormously, not only in the tilling and treatment of the soil and in the development of big irrigation projects to bring water and fertility to land that was formerly too dry for farming; it has also brought help to every step of the farming process, from spraying the fields and harvesting and grading of the crop, to storing, preserving, and transporting it. Machinery has released for the production of human food many hundreds of thousands of acres that formerly went for the feeding of draft horses and mules.

Tremendous progress has been made in the field of breeding new or improved varieties of plants and animals. Grains that will give a higher yield per plant, grains that will ripen earlier and produce in a climate that was too cold for the former slower-growing varieties, these have helped to open up new productive areas in cool climates; grains that will ripen all their plants at the same time and grow to a uniform height have helped to develop more efficient use of harvesting machinery. The same is true for cotton and other crops. Crops have been bred with improved food values: grains richer in high-quality protein, squash rich in vitamin A, tomatoes rich in vitamin C, and others.

Many kinds of crops have been developed, including such staples as beans, potatoes, cabbages, and grains, with an inbred resistance to their own specific diseases. This may some day offer an effective substitute for dangers of widespread spraying with the deadly modern pesticides.

Animal breeding has kept pace with the progress in plant breeding, producing cows that give richer milk, as well as cattle and hogs that produce more and better meat on less feed. In 1915 an average farm flock of hens might produce 56 eggs in a year from each member. Today a good flock should produce 200 eggs or more per layer.

With all these improvements in quality it is easy to credit the breeder with more than his share of the advance. Feeding and management play a very important part in the improvement. It has been shown that a proper balance in the chemistry of a fertilizer can play an important part in the quality of a crop, so that hay, grown on a properly balanced fertilizer, will produce more meat per pound of feed than a much larger crop of hay raised on a poorly balanced fertilizer.

Having produced superior animals, the farmer can greatly increase their usefulness by proper sanitation and housing and the control of temperature, humidity, and other environmental conditions which can promote fast growth and high productivity. Having produced superior crops and animals, man can greatly increase their value to himself through his new knowledge of nutrition. Just as, with fertilizers, a proper balance of the different elements will affect both the size and the quality of the crop, so with the diet of humans and other animals, a proper balance of the nutrient elements will produce a more effective food.

Finally, among the important advances toward making the most of a nation's food supply, the processing, the preserving and distribution of food have contributed their indispensable share. New methods of preservation by freezing and dehydration have improved the quality and reduced the losses of foods to be stored. Accurate control of temperature, moisture, and air chemistry has increased the ability to store fresh fruits and vegetables. Plastic wrapping has eliminated much destruction by insects. Refrigerated transportation by plane, ship, and train has helped greatly to expand and preserve the available food supply.

Florida has given a dramatic example of the many-sided efforts that may go into the building of a single new food-producing industry. For generations, men have attempted to raise cattle on the vast Florida prairies, but they never were able to raise beef that was fit to eat. On the richest-looking grass ranges the cattle still seemed to starve. Finally, in the 1940's, it was discovered that the soil lacked one essential element—cobalt. The cattle did not need the cobalt for themselves, but the bacteria that helped them to digest their food did need it. The addition of an ounce or two to a ton of hay made a startling difference in the health of the cattle. New, more nutritious grasses were introduced on the ranges. These helped, but the humid heat and the cattle ticks still proved a handicap to the native breeds of cattle which thrived so well in other parts of the country.

Brahman cattle were brought to Florida from India; unlike the native cattle, these have the ability to sweat, and so were better able to stand the new climate. The Florida ticks seemed to find the Brahmans less palatable as hosts, thus removing another handicap for the cattleman, but still something was lacking. These cattle tended to be nervous and aggressive, and the taste of their meat was as unpalatable to humans as it was to the ticks. Finally, through scientific crossing with such breeds as the Hereford, the Black Angus, the Santa Gertrudis, and others, a type was produced that could thrive in the Florida environment and was also manageable, productive, and palatable. Thus, by bringing together the needed qualities in plants and animals from the far corners of the earth and breeding and managing them with scientific skill, a great new area of land was made productive. A new food-producing industry was developed.

So much for the United States. Much the same kind of story is true for the other developed nations. How much of this kind of progress can be brought to the less developed, hungry nations of the earth? We will consider this in a later chapter, but here it is well to remember that the potentials for food production depend very largely on the climate, on the kind and the amount of soil and water that is available, and on the knowledge of crops and management methods that can succeed under these conditions. But statistics on the amount of available soil mean little until we know how the productive land is used. Huge areas of the earth's surface have been destroyed by overuse and wrong use of the fertile soil, and more is still being ruined every year.

Healthy soil protects and renews itself. Plant roots tie it in place, holding against erosion by wind and rain, filling it with an organic sponge to absorb the rain and feed the growing plants. This living soil, with its plants, is the factory that produces the earth's food. When man breaks its protective cover of vegetation with the plow, it becomes vulnerable to erosion by wind and rain. Now, for his own survival, man must protect it. Contour plowing can help to check the erosion, holding the runoff in level furrows. Strip farming can interpose protective barriers of sod between the exposed strips of plowland. The soil's health can be maintained by plowing in crops of clover or other nitrogen gatherers.

Some fine soils are very vulnerable to erosion by wind. In dry areas such soils require a dependable cover of sod. Millions of acres of such land have been plowed and planted to wheat. In a dry season, when the wheat fails to mature, the unprotected soil may be carried away by the wind. In the drought of the 1930's millions of tons of good topsoil were picked up by the wind from the dust bowl of the midwest and carried a thousand miles to be dumped in the Atlantic Ocean.

The unplowed lands can contribute their crops of forage to raise sheep and cattle; but when too many animals are put to graze too heavily, the plants die under this abuse, while the hoofs destroy the sod and so contribute their share to the creation of new deserts. From such deserts the blowing sand moves out to destroy the surrounding grass and so spreads the destruction; it has been estimated that in some places the edge of the Sahara desert is moving outward by as much as 30 miles a year. When water is available this dry land can be made productive by irrigation, but irrigation entails special hazards. Water that is drawn from the earth may carry chemicals dissolved from the soil particles, and as it evaporates on the irrigated fields it leaves these chemicals behind. These may slowly accumulate to poison the land until no crops can survive on it. The earth carries huge areas of desert built in this way by man from once fertile soil, and it carries other areas that are now fated to become desert unless the process of destruction can be checked.

Enough is known about the proper management of land to avoid this wanton destruction. But good management is costly. It requires the proper tools, as well as the knowledge and the incentive to use the land wisely. In countries around the world, where people without knowledge or resources are driven by hunger to overuse the land, the process of deterioration continues. India, for example, has nearly a quarter billion cattle. These, together with sheep and goats, have grazed the land so heavily in some areas as to destroy the protecting sod. While they destroy the forage cover, they return to the land each year, in the form of manure, nearly a quarter billion tons of fertilizer. This might be very helpful, but in some areas the crowding population—having cut off their forests and having no firewood—use this essential fertilizer for cooking their food. Thus the misuse of the land spirals back on itself, reducing the ability of the land to support life.

Among the regions of the world with large areas of fertile and productive agricultural land, continental Western Europe, continental United States, and India stand out. Western Europe is already highly developed and will need all its prospective productivity to feed its own people. India has great potentials for expanding its output of food, but a small present prospect of producing enough for its own fast-growing needs.

The report of the U.S. Department of Agriculture just cited concluded that arable land per capita is declining in every region while per capita grain production in the less-developed world is lower today than it was before World War II. Agricultural potential is now concentrated in North America which is also emerging as the world's breadbasket. In 1960–1961, North America's net regional exports totaled 39 million tons which, based upon current trends, will rise to 58 million tons in 1980 and 94 million tons by the year 2000.

Viewing these prospects against the background of the present unrest and instability in the world, it becomes clear that the future of the world's food supply is a vital interest of the United States. It would seem clear that, like it or not, the United States is an integral part of the world community from which there is no escape; that in this environment the finding of a solution to this world problem is a matter of life and death to all mankind.

CHAPTER VIII

Natural Resources

In the twentieth century man has learned a lot about the management of the earth for the production of food, but land is not the only natural resource needed to support life. As the earth becomes cluttered with the debris of civilization it is suddenly apparent that boundless supplies of air and water can no longer be taken for granted. Man has still a lot to learn about the management of these resources. The air over our big cities becomes unfit to breathe, a hazard to human health. Water, when it is available, is often unfit for human use.

In 1966 a committee of the National Academy of Sciences reported that about 65 million tons of carbon monoxide is poured into the air of the United States each year. A study in the city of Los Angeles showed that the automobiles in that single city poured 9,000 tons of carbon monoxide into the air every day.

On a drive across the United States, past city after city, one passes great clouds of discolored smoke rising from factories, steel mills, chemical plants, pulp mills, and dozens of others, all blending into the pall of haze that stretches across the nation. Thirty years ago, the air was clear and exhilarating. The total of all these aerial poisons approaches two hundred million tons each year, but they do not all stay in the air. With every breath, the nation's people draw these poisons into their lungs. And these poisons are a factor in the alarming increase in emphysema, lung cancer, and bronchitis.

Cigarettes no doubt contribute more than their share to the poisons that ruin lungs and other vital organs; but the use of cigarettes is a matter of free choice for each individual. The poisons that go into the air are inescapable and create a serious health hazard to every individual. St. Louis and Los Angeles have showed that much of this pollution can be eliminated through the control of incinerators and industrial smoke. It seems likely that automobile exhausts can be at least partly controlled. The equipment for control of much of this pollution is expensive. The prospects for a doubling of the population within 35 years certainly lends urgency to the efforts of the federal and state governments to hold this poisoning of the air within limits that the human lungs can tolerate. Vegetation, too, can be seriously affected by these poisons.

Water is another essential natural resource that once seemed inexhaustible. The immediate problem is not so much with the total amount of water, as with getting it to where it is needed, storing it, and maintaining a quality that is fit for use. But it has been estimated that by 1980 the nation's need will have outgrown the total dependable supply.

The United States receives from the air an enormous amount of water each year. It has been estimated that on the average it receives enough to cover the entire country to a depth of 30 inches. This amounts to a total of about 1,430 cubic miles. But this water is received in very uneven amounts. In some parts of the country the rainfall averages over sixty inches. In other parts it is less than ten. The nation as a whole faces a critical shortage that is already hampering the development of some areas and has caused bitter court battles between the affected states.

In many areas the water is being pumped from the ground much faster than it is being recharged, so that the level of the underground reservoir is dropping to the point where the cost of pumping makes its use prohibitive. It was reported in April, 1964, that 320,000 acres of farmland in Arizona had been withdrawn from production on account of the water shortage. But this is only the beginning of the story. Research has shown that when the water level is drawn down in certain types of soil the earth will settle, fill the empty spaces, and thus permanently lose a large part of its capacity to store water. To say that the average rainfall is 30 inches tells only a part of the story. Out of this 30-inch total it is estimated that 20 inches—equal to 1,000 cubic miles of water—is lost back into the air by evaporation and by evapotranspiration (the combination of evaporation and transpiration from vegetation). Of the remaining ten inches, equal to 390 cubic miles, nearly eight runs out to sea as streamflow from the 48 contiguous states. This leaves only a comparatively small amount to go into the ground to recharge the natural underground reservoirs as they are drawn down by overuse.

The amount of this recharge is greatly affected by the treatment or mistreatment of the soil surface. The ability of the soil surface to absorb the rainfall depends largely on its cover of absorbent humus that is built up through the ages by vegetation and the work of insects and other animal forms that disintegrate it and mix it with the soil. When forests are cut or grasslands plowed or overgrazed, this absorbent cover may be damaged or destroyed, and the soil thus loses much of its power to "take in" the rain. In addition to overdrawing from the earth's store of water, man compounds his own problem when he hurts the power of the land to replace the water that he has taken. On top of this, about a million acres each year are being taken out of the business of absorbing water, and are given a waterproof cover of cement for roads, airports, city streets and houses, and instead of going into the earth the water runs off to create floods and waste itself in the ocean.

The water that is transpired by the plants is not all wasted, of course, as transpiration is a basic part of the process of food production. It takes about 1,000 pounds of water to produce a single pound of irrigated corn or sugar; 1,500 pounds for a single pound of wheat; and 10,000 pounds for a pound of cotton fiber.

The huge demands of industry take almost as much of the water supply as agriculture, but, unlike agriculture, industry returns a far larger share back to the streams or soil. Much of this industrial water is badly polluted but can be cleaned by proper treatment and used again. Home and other municipal uses take less than a tenth of the total that is used for farm and factory, and most of this is returned again to its sources after use. Altogether, it takes about 1,700 gallons a day to meet the needs of the average American.

When communities were small and discharged their filth into the rivers, the flowing water diluted and oxidized the pollution with the help of plants and animal life, so that little harm was done. But with the crowding growth of population, the pollution became more than the streams could absorb. The cleansing plants and fish were killed, and many streams lost the power to cleanse themselves, becoming little better than open sewers. Each community discharged its filth into the streams with little thought for its neighbors downstream. The river continued from city to city—each in its turn discharging into the water the untreated wastes from its sewers and industrial plants, and sending it along for the next city to clean up and use again for washing and drinking. Some cities have been using water that had already been used in this way as much as five times before reaching them. For a single example, in March, 1966, the city of Omaha reached agreement with state and federal officials to reduce the discharge of offal from its slaughterhouses into the Missouri River. This had amounted to 200 tons a day of undigested stomach contents from slaughtered animals and 60 tons a day of waste grease which had been clogging the inlets of St. Joseph's city water system 100 miles downstream.

In 1963 there were more than 1,500 communities with a population of 13 million people that were discharging untreated sewage into their streams. Another 1,500 communities were discharging inadequately treated sewage from 17 million people. More than 2,700 small towns with nearly 6 million people did not even have sewage treatment installations.

The sewage entering the streams is obvious and harmful. The invisible seepage from millions of septic tanks also contributes its unseen share. To realize how polluted water from these tanks can move through the ground, one has only to consider the suds that have appeared in the drinking water of many areas where detergents from laundry and household use have spread through the ground from septic tank to water supply. The suds can be controlled by the prohibition of the hard detergents that make them, as many states are now doing by legislation. But the pollution from the sewage is not so easy to control. In 1963, seventy-five million people still depended on septic tanks, and many of these are not adequately effective. In 1965 it was estimated by the U.S. Public Health Service that the cost of replacing obsolete facilities, improving treatment standards, and extending sewage collection systems for new urban and suburban developments would come to about $1.6 billion per year for the rest of the decade.

One of the very serious and complex forms of pollution is that from the modern pesticides such as DDT. A great deal of research has gone into testing these chemicals in the effort to find safe ways of using them, but there is still much to be learned before their use can be considered safe, and they are still showing up in air, water, and food and in the bodies of fish and wildlife which they have poisoned.

The action of some of these pesticides is subtle and long-lasting. They are not eliminated from the body as most poisons are, but remain stored in fat, in the brain, and in other parts. Even when taken in very small, apparently harmless amounts, they may thus accumulate in the body over a period of time and build up to dangerous concentrations.

Dr. M. M. Hargraves of the Mayo Clinic and the University of Minnesota, referring to some 200 case histories of cancer and blood diseases, expressed the conviction that they show a direct cause and effect relationship to the chlorinated hydrocarbons which include DDT and many others. There have also been instances where people exposed to organophosphorous insecticides have developed schizophrenic and other reactions including impairment of memory.

These poisons are spread for great distances in uncanny ways. Concentrations have been found in halibut and tuna off the coasts of North America. This may sound incredible, until one remembers that a great deal of the poison is spread by dusting from airplanes, for both forests and farm crops, and remembers also that during the dust storms of the 1930's great quantities of dust were blown from the midwest out over the Atlantic. Many tests have shown how these poisons may be accumulated and passed on in concentrated form from one living organism to another. At Big Bear Lake in California, toxaphene, a chlorinated hydrocarbon, was applied to the water at the rate of 0.2 parts per million. This was absorbed by the plankton organisms in the water and concentrated to a level of 73 parts per million. Fish that ate the plankton built up the concentration to 200 parts per million, and a fish-eating bird, a pelican, contained 1,700 parts per million. Plankton collected at the lake and fed to trout in a hatchery poisoned the trout. In its review of its 1963 pesticide research program, the Department of the Interior reported that oysters exposed to DDT in their environment accumulated concentrations 70,000 times as strong in their bodies within about a month.

A report released by the Public Health Service of the Department of Health, Education, and Welfare contained an estimate that in 1963 water pollution killed about 7.8 million fish. Industrial operations, the largest identified cause, killed about 3.2 million; next came municipal sewage with a kill of over a million, and agricultural operations with more than 760,000. One of the heaviest kills, in the Mississippi River, was traced to endrin, one of the pesticides, which apparently came to the river from an industrial plant. Similar kills in the Mississippi have taken place at the same time of year every year for four years. What does this mean for New Orleans and other cities that depend on the river for their water supply? Studies by the Massachusetts Department of Fisheries and Game, covering eleven reservoirs that serve as public water supplies, showed that the fish in all of them were heavily contaminated, with concentrations ranging from an average of 35.4 parts per million up to 96.7 parts for two of them. This is 14 times the legal tolerance for DDT in foods.

At the Patuxent Wildlife Research Center at Beltsville, Maryland, sublethal doses of DDT given to mallard ducks, quail, and pheasants caused marked changes in the tissue structure of the reproductive organs, lowered reproductive ability, and increased the number of cripples and the mortality among the young that did hatch. Field studies at Michigan State College have shown that DDT sprayed on elms in the fall can be carried through the winter by earthworms that eat the sprayed leaves. These worms, when eaten by robins in the spring, can pass along enough poison to wipe out the entire population of robins for the area, including any eggs or young produced before the parents were finally sterilized or killed by the poison.

These modern poisons have become almost indispensable for the farmer, as the vast increase in food crops has led to the buildup of huge insect populations. However, it must also be borne in mind that the poisons, like narcotics, tend to enslave their users, for they kill not only the harmful insects, but in most cases kill also the useful creatures which normally help to control the pests and are a basic natural resource. A vivid example of this was given in the orange groves of California. Here, as the industry expanded in the last century, the cottony cushion scale found the food it needed to increase enormously, until it became a serious threat to the industry. This scale is believed to have been introduced from Australia, and in the United States, where it was free from the controlling influence of the insects that had kept it in check in Australia, it put on its own population explosion. This all happened within the short space of fifteen years from the time of its first discovery in California. Finally, in 1888 a search was made in Australia for the insects that controlled it, and two species were brought back; a tiny fly *(Chryptochaetum iceryae)* and the vedalia lady beetle *(Rodolia cardinalis)*. These soon multiplied on their abundant food supply and brought the scale completely under control. This effective control continued until after the Second World War, when DDT and other modern pesticides were used in the citrus groves against other pests. In the areas where they were used, these sprays eliminated the protecting beetles, and the cottony cushion scale soon returned in heavy infestations.

It has been common experience that, when used against mosquitoes, the sprays have had disappointing results of two kinds. They not only wiped out the minnows and other creatures that ate the mosquito larvae, they quickly produced mosquitoes that were immune to the poisons. They accomplished this by killing off all the mosquitoes that were susceptible to the poison, thus producing a deceptively comfortable freedom from the pests for a short time; meanwhile the few immune mosquitoes that had survived the spray soon built up huge new populations that were resistant to the poison, and now, with the natural controls gone or much reduced, the in-fested communities were, in many cases, worse off than ever.

These experiences are typical of many that are taking place throughout the world. In July, 1964, at a meeting of the 12th International Congress of Entomology in London, a resolution was passed to the effect that "profound environmental changes" caused by such factors as defoliation and the indiscriminate use of chemical pesticides would result in "the elimination of many species" and the emergence of "vast reservoirs of insect pests."

Obviously, although pesticides have become an essential factor in the world's food production, there is still much to be learned about their proper use. One major need now is to develop poisons that will kill only the specific creatures at which they are aimed. This is now being done successfully with rats and mice. Equally if not more important is the development of biological control methods, such as the breeding of plants that are resistant to disease. This has also been done successfully in many cases. There has been limited success also with the breeding of plants that can resist insect attacks. In some cases, as with the screw worm, the breeding and release of millions of sterilized males to monopolize the females has been very effective. But methods of biological control are greatly handicapped, as we have seen, when the controlling organisms are killed off by the widespread poisons.

It has become obvious that, as our population builds up, this changes the whole environment of life. In this new environment biological law dictates that, to survive, human life must adapt itself to the new conditions. The right of the individual or community to treat the air and water and other life-supporting natural resources as their own private property, to be used as one pleases, has come into head-on collision with the rights of all other people and communities to protect these resources for the good of all. The right of the city or industrial plant to pollute the river that brings it life is modified by the rights of its neighbors downstream. The cost of using these resources, yet still maintaining them in condition to continue their vital functions, has become too great for any individual to bear. It has to become a community project. But how does one define a community?

The quality and the value of a river depend not on just one particular community along its banks. The Mississippi River, for example, draws its water from a watershed area covering one and a quarter million square miles. Everything that happens to affect the streams on this vast area contributes to affect the quality, the volume, the steadiness, or the pollution of the river. The farmer whose pesticides wash in to poison the stream, the city whose sewage pollutes it, the industry whose chemicals poison it, the burned and bulldozed watershed whose eroded silt chokes its channel, each contributes what may be an insignificant fraction to the problem of the whole river, but these fractions multiplied by thousands become overwhelming. A thousand miles downstream, New Orleans receives the poisoned water for drinking. Millions of fish, killed by the poisons, add their offal to the mixture. The eroded silt clogs the river waterway, the sewage makes the water undrinkable. Each community that insists on its private right to independent action becomes a hazard to the welfare of the others. As far as the water is concerned, the whole vast watershed has become one community faced with a choice of chaos or of responsible correlated management. On the Mississippi system the problem is perhaps chiefly one of maintaining water quality that is fit for use. On other rivers, notably the Colorado and the Rio Grande, the problem is to find and distribute enough water for the survival of the growing communities.

The Ruhr district of West Germany has had, in very intense form, the problems both of water shortage and water pollution. It is one of the busiest and most crowded spots in the Western World. Its underlying political and economic problems are quite similar to those of the United States, and yet it has achieved an outstanding success in meeting these problems and in making the most effective use of the water that is available. This success applies not only to the municipal and industrial uses, but also to a growing recreational use, and it is worth remembering that this use is becoming increasingly important in the United States. It has been estimated by the Outdoor Recreation Resources Review Commission that by the year 2000 A.D. swimming will have passed driving for pleasure as the most popular outdoor recreation.

The United States has the technical knowledge and financial resources to duplicate this successful management. The chief obstacle appears to lie in the problem of finding effective working relationships between the various public and private agencies concerned, and in working out some acceptable method of allocating the costs and benefits among the multitude of different interests that are involved.

A river is a physically indivisible unit, but along its course it is divided politically into many segments. When one of these segments that has, for generations, dumped its sewage into the river finds another community growing up downstream, it may be reluctant to tax itself hundreds of thousands or millions of dollars for the benefit of the new community. As the nation grows, the problem is to find a successful way of adjusting the differences and meeting the costs. This problem has been met in the Ruhr by entrusting almost complete authority over water quality and quantity to two groups of associations, one being concerned primarily with control of pollution and the other with the development and distribution of water resources.

These associations operate somewhat like English and American cooperatives, with three important differences: 1) membership is compulsory; 2) voting power is apportioned among members in accord with the size of their contributions; and, 3) charges and assessments are as binding as taxes. One key to success here is the provision that the costs of constructing and operating the system are to be paid by those members whose activities make it necessary and by those who benefit from it. There are rather detailed provisions or formulas for working this out on questions of land drainage, waste disposal, and water supply.

The ability to plan and manage an entire river system as a unit through a cooperative formula that includes all the users has added greatly to the efficiency and economy of the undertaking, but there is still the growing problem of water shortage which must grow with the increase of population. The United States needs better provisions for cleaning and reusing the water as many times as possible before it reaches the ocean. Better storage and better management of the watersheds can reduce losses by seepage and by evaporation. Tests at some reservoirs in Arizona have shown evaporation losses ranging from four to nearly ten feet in a year. There are possibilities in pumping water underground for storage away from the sunlight as well as for covering reservoirs with a thin film to prevent evaporation.

One of the most important of the problems connected with the water supply is the management of the forest watersheds, where most of the water originates and where much of it is stored. These forests are important as builders and protectors of the soil, for the invaluable timber they produce, and for the water which, in many cases, is even more valuable; in some areas they supply important forage for sheep and cattle, and they are becoming increasingly important for their recreational use and as wildlife refuges. These uses are not all compatible. Stock raising can severely damage a forest. Under some conditions the type of management that produces the best timber harvest does not give the highest yield of water. Each tree uses a considerable amount of water in its growth, and some kinds use more than others. Thus the number and the types of trees raised on a watershed will directly affect the amount of water that it will yield. A forest that has been recently harvested loses much of its attractiveness for recreational use. The problem in management of publicly owned forests is to get the best combination or multiple use of the different values for which it may be fitted.

Each nonrenewable mineral or chemical resource in the earth presents its own special problem. Some, like petroleum and coal, appear to be available in quantities that will take care of prospective needs for some time to come. Others, like lead, tin, and zinc have much less promising reserves in sight. Discoveries of new supplies, techniques, or substitutes, may make present estimates obsolete. One thing is certain, though: As the new nations build their economies and multiply their populations and their needs, the demand for raw materials is going to become far more pressing, and the competition between nations for essential sources of supply is going to become more critical.

Of all the natural resources, space for living, like air and water, once appeared inexhaustible. There is still a lot of open space on the surface of the earth, but every day it becomes clearer that living space means far more than space for houses and the production of food and other supplies for their occupants. Life for these occupants means more than food and supplies. We will have to learn how much space and what kind of space man needs for the kind of life that gives room for his spirit to grow and for him to find rewards in the living. And we will have to learn how to make far better use of our remaining space than we have yet done.

CHAPTER IX

Employment

A job is a three-way relationship between the consumer whose wants make it possible, the employer who creates it and manages it, and the worker who exchanges his abilities for a share of what the consumer is able or willing to pay. This three-way relationship is a form of competition. The consumer wants to get as much as he can, as cheaply as possible; the worker must support his family and prepare for the future; and the employer, between these two opposing forces, must save enough to support himself, supply the equipment, pay the wages and taxes, and insure against the risks and losses which face every business and bankrupt many of them. If, over the long run, these conditions are not met, the jobs tend to evaporate.

This is the simple physical structure of the job, but its roots spread far deeper and wider than that. The job is a symbol of status and security which supports the self-respect and citizenship of its owner. At whatever level, it confers a sense of responsibility and belonging. It adds to the buying power of the community, which supports the public welfare, and, by the mere furnishing of occupation for restless energy, it is man's best antidote for crime and juvenile delinquency.

At every step in this relationship there are human lives and public welfare involved. Unhappy experience has proved that these cannot safely be trusted to the uncertain fortunes of the contest between the opposing forces. A major function of government is to establish principles and policies which will help to maintain a healthy balance between the three and still leave each as free as possible to contribute its necessary share toward the welfare of the whole. The nation has had much experience with attempts to maintain this balance in the past fifty years. It has had some success and still has a lot to learn.

In the depression of the 1930's the industrialized nations dropped from a very high level of employment to a very low one, due in large part to blind psychology. First a wave of hysterical optimism led to speculative overproduction, wild speculation in the stock market, and a general overexpansion of debts, coupled with very high employment. When a few big debts overwhelmed insolvent debtors, a complete reversal took place. Creditors called for payments from debtors whose assets had consisted largely of unjustified hopes. With a general loss of confidence and widespread bankruptcies, construction, production, and employment evaporated and depression, feeding on itself, spread in a downward spiral. Among the hardest hit of its victims was the farmer.

This depression would eventually have cured itself when consumer needs built up again, but the cure would have been at a terrible cost in hardship and broken lives. The recovery was started earlier, partly through the psychological stiffening administered by a great leader and partly by heavy government spending which injected new buying power into the pockets of the citizens. Many steps have been taken to forestall the development of another such experience. These include a stronger banking system, legal safeguards to control speculation in stocks with borrowed money, a gathering of statistical information that helps to take the gamble out of farming, and the agricultural adjustment program which helped to restore farm buying power and put the prostrate farmers back on their feet. The strengthening of labor unions helped to maintain the flow of buying power from the employer into the pockets of the mass consumer.

One major change in the nation's way of life was not so easy to control. This was the movement from farm to city. We have already seen how research and invention increased the efficiency of farm labor until, by 1962, the work of one farm laborer could feed twice as many people as in 1940. As the worker's output increased, the number needed to feed the nation declined; millions of the resulting jobless streamed to the cities, with no training or preparation for industrial work. In 1940 there had been 30.5 million people living on farms in the United States. By 1962 this number had dropped to 15.6 million. This meant that 15 million people who had been self-sufficient, engaged in feeding themselves and their fellow citizens, could no longer be so. They must now find some way to exchange their brains and strength for food produced by someone else. They must find jobs.

This was their hard personal problem, but for the nation as a whole it meant a revolution in its way of life. With the loss of 15 million jobs that required little training or education, the country had lost a safety valve which might have absorbed the untrained, uneducated millions of young people who were not fitted for the skilled jobs offered by industry.

The result was a tremendous increase in the demand for jobs, and this was multiplied by the explosive increase in the nation's population, as the waves of young people reached employment age each year faster than new jobs could be created. By June, 1963, the number of people holding jobs had passed 70 million, but there were still 4.2 million unemployed, and the nation's labor force, the number of people holding or seeking jobs, was growing by more than a million a year. Among these unemployed there were over a million teen-agers, the highest unemployment rate for this group since records have been kept, and, among them, one out of every four Negroes desiring work was unemployed, compared with only one out of every six whites.

While these figures represented only a small fraction of the nation's people, they were concentrated chiefly in localized groups where they had very great meaning. In some of the depressed areas of the Appalachian and Great Lakes regions, the overall unemployment rate ran as high as 25%—and even higher in, for example, the Watts area of Los Angeles at the time of the savage Watts riots in 1965.

The nation had lived through the decade of the 1950's in a dream, measuring its health by the growth of material wealth, and pretty well satisfied with its achievement. Suddenly, like the eruption of a disease at the end of its time of incubation, a wave of uneasiness struck the nation. Millions of young people, born in the population boom of the 1940's, were flooding the overcrowded school systems and beginning to look for jobs. The old traditional pool of unskilled jobs on the land was gone. The schools were not equipped to meet the demands for job training. Prejudice made this deficiency especially hard on the nonwhites who most needed the training.

The great need for more jobs met in head-on confrontation with the wholesale destruction of jobs by the growing force of automation. The President's Manpower Report of March, 1964, forecast that during the next seven years a net increase of 11 to 12 million jobs would be needed to provide employment for the new additions to the labor force and to reduce unemployment to a more acceptable level. In addition, there would be needed another two million jobs each year to replace those that would be destroyed by increasing productivity, largely through automation. This would mean a total of not less than twenty-five or twenty-six million new jobs by 1970.

The huge spending of the "Great Society" program, supported by an enormous increase in debt, both public and private, has helped to make millions of new jobs and to buy time. By 1966 the demands of war had come near to producing a manpower shortage, and optimistic authorities were even predicting that automation would create more jobs than it destroyed. But as the world wakes up to the pressures of exploding populations fighting for food and jobs, it becomes clear that better answers will be needed.

Shortening the work week helps to spread the work opportunities. Rising wages lift the worker's buying power. Increased productivity through improving equipment and methods makes it possible to continue shortening the hours and increasing the wages in step with increasing productivity. But if the hours are shortened or the wages raised *beyond* this line of balance, the higher costs must eventually spread to affect the entire community, through the familiar self-defeating wage-price spiral. In this process some workers make immediate gains which may be illusory, because they lead to rises in the cost of living for everyone.

The Burroughs Corporation gave a single example of what has happened very widely as a result of rising costs in American industry. For several years it produced adding machines in two plants, one in Detroit and one in Scotland. The costs of production on identical products were 40% lower in Scotland than in Detroit, chiefly due to the difference in labor costs. It was actually cheaper to produce the machines in Scotland and then ship them back for sale in the United States. The result was a decision by the company to phase out the production in its Detroit plant and expand the production in Scotland. It was stated that the company employed more than 10,000 people in its plants abroad. The spiral of rising wages and prices had actually destroyed a lot of jobs in the United States. It affected not only those directly engaged in the production of the machines, but the hundreds or thousands of related jobs in the community that supported it, from grocery clerk, to lawyer, doctor, banker, and teacher.

In an attempt to keep costs and jobs in better balance, President Johnson established a set of guidelines based on the average increase in productivity in the United States. With this increase estimated at about 3.2% a year, it was felt that wages might be increased by not more than this amount in industries that could stand it, without throwing the nation's economic stability out of balance, and companies and unions were asked to respect this standard in their negotiations.

This guideline did not survive very long, and it is possible to estimate some measure of the effects from its breakdown. A group of union leaders in New York City asked for a wage raise on the bus and subway lines which far exceeded the guideline. At the beginning of January, 1966, a strike was called which stopped transportation on the city's bus and subway lines. For twelve days the union of 33,000 transit workers inflicted a strike which crippled a city of eight million, causing losses estimated at between $500 million and $1 billion, and caused untold hardship on the people who could not get to their work. The illegal strike was forbidden by court order, and the citizens of New York, watching on TV, saw the union leader tear up the court order, demand an impossible wage rise, and go to jail rather than compromise.

The resulting wage raise brought on a higher fare for users of the city transit system and a many-million-dollar increase in the budget deficit of the city. A year later the city was stirred by the news that some of its largest corporations were moving out, in spite of vigorous attempts by Mayor John V.

Lindsay to induce them to stay. In February, 1967, the head of a large consulting firm, in announcing that his organization was conducting studies for corporations that were considering moving out of the city, stated: "A half dozen years ago we might have done six of these studies in an entire year, but in 1967 we may conduct 40 such studies." Among reasons given by corporate executives for moving were the problems of commutation, the rising crime rate, swollen welfare costs, and the subway strike. The announcement continued: "In 1950 there were about one million persons employed in manufacturing in New York City. By 1964 this figure had dropped 14% to 865,000 workers. . . . New York City has lost an average of two million man-days through strikes every year since World War II. That's about five times the comparable rate in many other large cities."

Each individual worker feels the pinch of rising costs, and is entitled to a raise to meet them. But when raw organized power can force a great city to pay beyond its ability, many a job destroys itself in the process. The successful transit strike was followed by a number of other strikes by public service workers in the city, all no doubt contributing their share to the outflow of businesses and jobs in 1967.

The process of collective bargaining seems to have reached the point where it must find some formula which will protect the public interest in the confrontation between the private interests of the two groups which do the bargaining. Failing that, some form of binding arbitration would seem to be essential. Compulsory arbitration has two weaknesses. First, as a threat to freedom of action, it is opposed by both labor and management. Second, it would bring politics more closely than ever into the problems of labor relations. Each side would feel more strongly the need to have men in government who could be depended on to favor its point of view.

One of the hopeful efforts to find a formula for responsible labor-management relations lies in the field of profit-sharing, or progress-sharing, which offers to each side some tangible benefit from cooperation with the other. There are thousands of such programs in operation in the United States, with other thousands coming into being each year.

One widely discussed plan is that which was put into operation by the Kaiser Steel Company at Fontana, California, as an outgrowth of the disastrous steel strike of 1959. It has these basic features: 1) There is an ironclad guarantee that no worker will be fired because a machine takes over his job. If the job is destroyed by a machine, he is placed in a reserve pool at full pay for one year or until a new opening comes up. With an 8% annual turnover in employment there are many new openings. 2) Beyond this job security, the workers under this plan receive nearly a third of all savings from increased productivity in the plant, whether it comes from automation or any other improvement in efficiency which cuts the cost of production. Thus each worker shares in the benefits of increased efficiency by the whole team. As a part of this progress-sharing the company receives a four-year pledge against strikes.

This Kaiser plan has been managed by a nine-man committee, with three members representing the workers, three to represent the management, and three neutral members. In the event of any unsettled dispute the three neutral members have the final decision. This plan may not be adequate to meet the test of a real depression, and it does not solve the menace of a large scale destruction of jobs by machines or of the coming flood of new job seekers. It does, however, contain the principles of a cooperative, mutually beneficial approach to the problems of a single plant and offers the means for a continuing study of these problems by informed and responsible people. Its final success depends on the determination by each side to get away from the destructive crises that have damaged both so severely in the past.

We see another side of this solution in the case of the American Motors Company, which, in the time of its prosperity, set up a progress-sharing plan with its employes. Later, when the prosperity went into a slump, the plan must have appeared a good deal less attractive to the employes.

As the nation grows we see the three-way relationship between worker, employer, and consumer changing, with the concentrated power of the huge corporation and the huge labor union tending to overshadow the consumer (who, in fact, really includes both the other groups in their roles as private citizens.) The corporations are in many ways controlled by law in their relations with both consumer and worker. The unions, with some special immunities under the law, have grown so powerful that their monopoly gives them temporary control of the consumer. This was made clear in the New York transit strike, and the airline strike in 1966. It is a major problem in many other activities where the public welfare is in the hands of a few powerful labor leaders. Legislators have struggled with laws designed to enforce responsibility for the public interest on both business and union leaders with indifferent success. The growing complexity and vulnerability of society makes such legal responsibility a pressing need.

The need also grows for a more flexible and dependable way of reaching a fair division between the interests of the worker, the consumer, and the employer. Each year the use of raw power contributes less to the public interest.

Government—federal, state, and local—seems destined to play a steadily growing role in the creation of jobs, and to be steadily more deeply involved in the confrontation between the three sides that go into their making. In 1962 more than a quarter of all employment was generated by the government. The total employment for that year, including 2.7 million on active duty in the armed forces, came to 70.7 million. Of this total, 12 million were in government service, and 6.5 million more were employed in jobs generated by government purchases of goods and services, making altogether 18.5 million jobs created by government. Besides this, the Federal Government financed about 60% of all research and development programs in private industry and about 65% of all such programs in colleges and universities. About 90% of all research and development in the aircraft and aerospace industry, for example, was financed by the Federal Government.

Between 1947 and 1963 the number employed by state and local governments doubled, rising from 3.6 to 7.2 million. Education alone accounted for 3,254,000 state and local government jobs in 1962, having risen from 1,873,000 in ten years. Health and hospitals accounted for 722,000 state and local jobs in 1962, up from 432,000 in ten years.

Government spending to create jobs and buying power has been an effective tool to relieve serious unemployment. This success, together with the fast-multiplying expenses for public welfare programs, has led to the insistent interest in the idea of a guaranteed annual wage, or payment to bring the income of everyone up to a minimum standard level, regardless of the amount of work contributed in return. With all the obvious objections, the unavoidable abuses, and the psychological hazards that such a program could carry with it, the growing complexity and vulnerability of human society seems destined to lead in the direction of some such form of social insurance. The question will then arise whether insatiable human nature can discipline itself to hold its living standard at a level that the economic system can support.

CHAPTER X

Economic Interdependence

In November, 1965, a small malfunction in a distant power plant brought life to a halt for many million people in the northeastern United States. Thousands of people were trapped between stations in stalled trains and in apartment buildings in stalled elevators. The operation of heating and ventilation systems was interrupted. Thousands of industrial plants and jobs based on electric power stopped. Fortunately the warm weather averted major damage to plumbing systems and human health. The trouble was overcome quickly before major harm was done, but the experience showed dramatically how closely our industrial society is woven together in a single indissoluble web of interlocking strands.

Scattered through this great paralyzed community there were farms and homes that were untouched by the crisis. With their own sources of light and heat, they were temporarily independent of that part of the social and economic structure. Here were two ways of life, the old and the new, appearing much the same on the surface, but completely different in their significance to society as a whole. Basically they represented the difference between the old self-sufficient, self-dependent way of life that supported a large part of the population a few decades ago and the great social and economic machine that enmeshes each individual as a small cog in a vast whole today.

Originally evolved as a system of free enterprise, energized by the incentives of boundless opportunity, the system had developed into a complex of huge cumbersome organizations fighting among themselves, each for its own interests, with little regard for the public interest, and often with little understanding of how closely their actions affected the welfare of society.

With the growth of population the functioning of the huge economic system that supports it becomes daily more complex. We will try to get the simplest possible picture of the web of interrelationships that go into the making of the jobs, the opportunities, and the economic forces that support the nation's life, and what relation they have to the running of our economic system. Consider the loaves of bread bought by every housewife in the land. Where do they come from? How do they get to the table? Why do they cost so much?

Most of these loaves come in a paper wrapper to protect against dirt and germs. This wrapper had its origin as part of a distant forest. While the trees were growing, the forest was watched over and protected against fire and insect pests. This required expensive machinery, including planes and equipment and trained men to handle them. The trees were harvested and transported to the mill by costly machinery, turned into pulp and then into paper. The wrapper was thus a product of several vast industries employing many thousands of people, working with very costly and complex equipment. At every step of the way it had to pay its minute share of the cost for labor, management, machinery, materials, scientific research, and taxes.

The bread protected by this wrapper came from a special kind of wheat, the product of a worldwide search by trained scientists seeking special qualities. They gathered strains of wheat that produced the best flour, that were resistant to specific diseases, were early maturing and resistant to cold. These qualities would open up new farmlands that could not produce the older, less hardy varieties. Other strains were collected that grew on short stalks, resistant to blow-down in bad weather, or stalks that grew to a uniform height, all at the same time. This facilitated the use of harvesting machinery with minimum waste. The collection of all these desirable qualities was the prelude to years of scientific interbreeding to develop strains that would combine them all into one plant and help to multiply the productivity of the farmer's land and labor. A large part of this production and breeding was done by government scientists supported by taxes which added their share to the costs of every industry and worker.

On the farm the wheat was subject to the risks of drought, hail, fire, insects, and other hazards. To stay in business the farmer must get enough for his crop to repay such losses and still support his family. He must buy or rent expensive cultivating, planting, and harvesting machinery, which, like the paper wrapper, is the product of another vast industry, reaching from the coal and iron mines, through the railroads, the steel mills and factories, the assembly plants, and dealers that handled the machinery—the army of men who did the work. Other men built the factories and risked their money on the chance that they would succeed—some to make fortunes and others to lose their all on the gamble.

From the farm the wheat is carried for storage to the elevator, which is constructed chiefly from the products of the giant metal and cement industries. At the elevator it must be maintained dry and free from moisture to prevent deterioration. It must be protected from weevils and other insect pests, and for this, aside from complicated machinery, it must call on the products of another giant industry, chemistry, with its costly research and processing.

Then came another step of transportation to the flour mill, which represents another vast industry with specialized machinery and knowledge, workers and management, competing for survival with other mills. From here, with the help of the sales organization, the flour may have taken many paths, from bakery to country store or supermarket, on its way to your table.

This piece of bread that you had for breakfast had contributed its share to the support of many thousands of jobs in many industries throughout the continent. No mean portion of it went into taxes along the way to support the government, to build the roads, to maintain the traffic, and run the communities of the nation. At every step along the way someone had to pay somebody else for the cost of the services and equipment that were used. At every step it contributed to the making of jobs.

How much did this all add up to? How much did this piece of bread cost? At every step along the way, from farm to table, it was possible to reach a fair estimate of its share of the costs involved, and of the risks of weather, disease, and market demand, whose occasional heavy losses are a part of the average cost.

In theory the forces of demand and supply would tend automatically to set the price at a level that would repay the cost of producing the bread. If too much was produced, the consumers would not buy it all; in that case the grocer must lower his price to tempt more buyers. If the price was forced too low to pay the farmer for his costs, some of the less efficient would be forced out of production, and people would have to pay more to get their share of the smaller supply. This theory did not consider the human and political costs which became increasingly heavy as the country filled up, and the farmer had special problems.

After the end of the First World War there was not enough demand to use the tremendous productive capacity that had been built on the farms during the war; but farming is a way of life as well as a business. Many farmers would rather go hungry on the farm than move to the city. Many hung on and hoped, by increasing their production, to make up for the smaller margin of profit. This only helped to increase the oversupply, and farm prices dropped disastrously in relation to the machinery and other products that the farmer must buy. Thousands mortgaged their farms to pay their bills, and, as prices continued to drop, thousands went bankrupt. Hundreds of banks which held the mortgages had to close their doors, and with them went the life savings of many depositors. To protect these depositors, banks were forced to foreclose on the bankrupt farms, and soon whole farm communities were up in arms to defy the law and protect their farm homes. Through a series of spiraling steps the flow of money and trade, the lifeblood of the community, had dried up.

Like the loaf of bread, each farm, each job that it supported had reached out through the arteries of life to support the life of the nation. Multiplied by many million, they were the life of the nation. Their loss played a major role in bringing on the great depression of the 1930's. In this situation it was socially and politically impossible to wait for the forces of supply and demand to bring the economy back to life. Popular discontent reached the boiling point and elected a leader committed to change.

Up to this point the nation, blessed with a superabundance of natural resources, had prospered spectacularly on a system of free enterprise that, within specific guidelines, gave full play to individual initiative and imagination. To those who succeeded under this system, it offered the best incentives and opportunities for the development of a good life. To those with less luck or ability it offered an equal opportunity to fail.

As resources and opportunities gravitated into the hands of the successful, the less successful and the failures grew in numbers until they became a power at the voting booth as well as a challenge to the conscience of the community. Now the question arose of how to adapt the system of free enterprise to survive under the imbalances and complexities that its own inherent weaknesses had brought about. What new forces could be injected into the environment that would help to maintain the automatic balance between demand and supply, to keep the lifeblood flowing through the community? A basic need here was to help the farmer to balance his output with the demands of the market, so that he could receive a life-supporting return for his work and risks. To do this the first need was to measure both the production and the demand for the major crops, and how much the prices of the important farm crops had dropped in comparison with the prices of the things the farmer had to buy. With that knowledge, how could the farm buying power be restored to "parity"?* To do this, the government would buy enough of the surplus crop from the farmer to take it off the market and would pay enough for it to bring the price up toward the level of parity with the things he had to buy. In return the farmer would reduce the size of his crop by a specified amount in the effort to bring it back into balance with the estimated demand.

This, of course, meant a double tax on everyone; it meant raising the price of food and cotton to artificially high levels, with the increased price to come out of the pockets of the community. It meant taxing everyone for the money to buy and store the crops in order to raise the prices, and it meant a tremendous investment for storage and for officials and a bureaucracy to manage and carry out the program. In effect it meant a transfer of wealth or buying power from one pocket to another. It meant a huge step away from free enterprise and toward a managed economy. To those who had been charged with the responsibility it appeared to be much-needed insurance against far worse conditions for everyone.

It was hoped that the problem of overproduction could eventually be brought under control, as the demand for food increased, and the farmer was thus put back on his own feet. For years the problem kept growing more costly as the increased prices tempted the farmer to raise more. In 1953 the federal budget showed expenses for agriculture and agricultural resources to be approximately $3 billion. By 1963 the figure had risen to approximately $7 billion, which was more than the entire federal budget deficit for the year, and the vast amount of money involved had helped to build a huge special-interest political influence. By 1966 growing world hunger and the foreign aid program had brought the demand into balance with the supply and reversed the nature of the farm problem.

With the farmer back on his feet, another section of the economy began to develop dangerous symptoms of oversupply. The unemployed jobseeker and the automatic machine that destroyed jobs met in head-on collision. In a period of record-breaking prosperity the resulting political and social unrest proved once again that the system of free enterprise is not automatically successful in our modern environment.

---

* Restored to the relationship based on average prices for the years 1910-1914—the parity price of each major commodity being based on its own average.

Once more the imbalance between demand and supply began to choke off the flow of buying power throughout the community, and once more the social and political fabric started to deteriorate.

Once more the basic answer of the government was to attempt a speedup in the flow of buying power, to build new demand and produce new jobs to meet the demand. This time the approach was more varied. In addition to the many government activities by which it channeled new money into the economy, it decreed the tax cuts of 1964 and 1965, thus reducing the drain of buying power from the economy.

In planning the program, it was estimated by the President's Council of Economic Advisers that a tax cut of $11.5 billion would stimulate the national economy enough to add $30 billion to the national annual output. This would come through a series of steps, each one stimulating and supporting the next. Individual incomes, being relieved of taxes, were expected to rise by about $10 billion, and of this more than $9 billion would be spent for goods and services. This would lead to more production by manufacturers and more employment, which would again stimulate more spending, so that the full effect would be to add about $18 billion to the national product.

This growth, in turn, would stimulate the building of more production equipment, more work by federal, state, and local governments, each step stimulating the next, to reach a final total of about $30 billion, all developing from the original $11.5 billion tax cut. By the end of 1965 this estimate had turned out to be quite accurate. It was estimated that this growth would create from two to three million more jobs over a period of two-and-a-half years. This policy of stimulating the economy through cutting taxes and deficit spending has given the economy a sharp boost and appears to have the approval of many leading economists and the business community. There is still to be faced the question of how long such a policy can stand up under the growing flood of jobseekers and the pressures for expanding it to unmanageable proportions.

Since the 1930's a great deal has been learned about the management of the nation's economic problems, and many economists feel that debt is no longer the problem it was once thought to be; that as the national economy grows, the debt can safely grow along with it, in about the same proportion, and that by borrowing money as needed, to be pumped back into the circulation of the community, the pace of business and employment and buying power for all can be adequately maintained. The problem is to control the debt within limits that the economy can support and still maintain enough credit in reserve to take care of any unexpected crisis. For example, in the years from 1929 to 1945, through the crises of depression and war, the net national debt multiplied fifteenfold, from $16.5 billion to $252.7 billion. The tremendously strong credit of the nation, based on its growing productive power, was able to absorb this debt without serious damage, while some other nations which attempted a similar course could not control disastrous inflation that greatly reduced the value of their currencies.

In 1963 the world saw an epidemic of problems with the shrinking value of money or, to put it another way, with the rising cost of living. In Brazil, the cost of living rose elevenfold from 1958 to 1964. In that short period the value of the *cruzeiro* had dropped so that it took eleven times as many to buy the same amount of food or clothing. In Indonesia the costs had increased ninefold in the same time. In the United States the rise had been slower, but in the years from 1940 to 1962 the cost of living had more than doubled, the dollar having lost more than half its buying power. Thus, the value of insurance, wages, money in the bank, and so on, had all dropped.

What has happened to reduce the value of the dollar in this way? Before the great depression the paper dollar certificates were redeemable in gold worth $16 an ounce. The piece of paper was worth as much as the gold it could be exchanged for. But in the depression there was not enough gold to go around to pay the huge demands of panicky people who wanted something more tangible than paper. In 1934, to meet this crisis, the dollar was devalued; now instead of being worth a sixteenth of an ounce of gold, it was worth only a thirty-fifth of an ounce. The government had repudiated a part of its debt, reducing the value of its promise to pay, and within the United States it would no longer redeem the paper dollar in gold at any price; although in dealings with foreign banking systems, the dollar was still interchangeable for gold at the reduced price. The effect of the devaluation is clear and simple, but why, after this, should the dollar's buying power again shrink to half its value between 1940 and 1962?

Since it is no longer convertible to gold, the dollar's value, like daylight saving, is partly a matter of psychology, a matter of habit, a sort of balance point between the many upward and downward pressures on it. When a tax cut or heavy government spending puts more money into circulation, people have more money to spend and are willing to pay more for the things they want to buy, and the storekeeper can get more dollars for the things he sells. The value of the dollar goes down. As people continue to buy, and there is a need for more clothes and autos and steel and for more workers to produce them, the unions can more effectively strike for higher wages, and the manufacturers raise their prices to meet the higher costs. The wage-price spiral goes up, and the dollar drops again. This process can be partially controlled; if the banks charge a little higher interest on the money they lend, people find it harder to borrow money to build houses and pay wages; the demand for money thus rises and the dollar becomes worth more. The same thing happens when taxes are raised to take money out of circulation.

By managing the buying power of money in this and other ways, the government can do a lot to influence the flow of business activity and employment, and during the early 1960's it was very successful in stimulating business activity and at the same time holding down the cost of living; but in the process the growing debts posed new hazards which, to many economists, made the cure look more menacing than the disease.

In our fast-changing and complex economy, figures have a way of becoming obsolete before they are printed, and different methods of figuring give somewhat different results, but these figures from the economic report of the President for January, 1964, show the developing trend since the end of the war in 1945: In 1945 the federal debt was $252.7 billion, by 1963 this debt had risen to $260.9 billion; meanwhile the state and local government debt had risen more than sixfold, from $13.7 billion up to $82.1 billion, and private debt had risen more than fivefold, from nearly $140 billion to more than $752 billion. For these three categories of debt there had been a total rise of more than $698 billion. On the federal debt alone the interest charges came to nearly $10 billion in 1963. It was estimated that the consumer debt charges in 1963 came to more than $59 billion, including both interest and repayments of principal. This, together with payments on mortgages of $22.9 billion, took more than 20¢ out of every spendable dollar after taxes, compared with only 6.7¢ from each dollar in 1946. Against these debts, individual savings amounted to $19.3 billion in 1963, thus modifying somewhat the impact of the heavy debt.

Clearly a good part of the buying power that built the national economy and made jobs since 1945 has been based on borrowed money, and a good part of today's potential buying power has to go, instead, into repaying the old debts and the interest on them. In the meantime we should remember that the nation has grown in its power to carry debt. This is best shown by what is called the gross national product, which represents the nation's total output of goods and services at market prices. In 1945 this amounted to $213.6 billion. By 1963 it had climbed to $585 billion, for a rise of $371.4 billion. But this increase was largely supported by the $689.3 billion rise in total debts. Even with its growing strength there would seem to be a limit to the debts and interest that the nation can carry without destroying the public confidence in the value of its money. If it were an isolated community, independent from the rest of the world, it might be able to go on for a long time in this way. But in its relations with other nations it has already overextended its credit, and some foreign nations, losing confidence in the future safety of the American dollar, have been cashing in their dollars for gold from the U.S. Treasury. At some level there is a psychological "flash point" where confidence turns to panic and people don't want the paper currency. Then the flow of international trade shrinks, and with it goes the loss of jobs and business at home. If such a point comes, it is essential that the government have a good reserve of credit to fall back on, to keep the wheels turning, to avoid the inflation that wipes out the value of money, of wages, of savings. We shall consider this question of the dollar in international trade further in Chapter XV.

We see, then, that the economic health of a nation is a structure of many interwoven strands, and the health of each is closely interdependent with the others. Like the mechanism of a watch, each contributes its all-important share. If any part breaks, the whole is affected. The welfare of each individual citizen depends on the successful functioning of the whole.

CHAPTER XI

Environment and the Human Community

For ten thousand years, under innumerable differences in environment, human communities have gone through their cycles of prosperity and decay, based largely on the condition of their human and natural resources. Today, under the pressures of scientific achievements and population growth, the conditions that shape human life and relationships are changing in ways that have never been experienced before. These changes have come so fast that man has fallen far behind in his efforts to understand and adjust his way of life to live with them.

The influence of these changes spreads out through many chain reactions that interact to produce widespread disharmony throughout the entire human community. We experience this disharmony chiefly through its points of crisis—economic depression, hunger, racial tension, war, and revolt; yet we seldom stop to see them for what they are: waves on a tide of chain reactions that started long ago and lead toward a distant future. The movement of this tide may be so slow as to be completely invisible to the individual on the spot, and the human attempt at a cure may thus sometimes have little relationship to the real problem.

This point becomes clear if we follow the tidal movements behind some of today's crises. How many of them start from the pervasive human instinct to let judgment be warped by personal interest! We see Thomas Jefferson working to build the Constitution of the United States, an instrument designed to insure freedom and equality of opportunity to all men who lived under it; and yet, to secure its adoption it required the signatures of slave owners, who would not have accepted the Constitution with obvious equivocation. It was no doubt the best attainable solution to a political dilemma. From it there flowed the tide that led later to the slaughter and devastation of the Civil War, and later still to the riots of the 1960's in communities whose members claim their rights yet deny the same rights to their fellows. And the tide still flows on.

The instinct for subconscious self-deception that lay behind this problem seems to be as much a basic part of the human environment as the weather or hunger or polluted water. In the world's population explosion we see another aspect of this instinctive refusal to face inconvenient facts. Advances in agriculture, medicine, and living conditions led to the much-desired results of making life safer and more comfortable; but the refusal of political and religious leaders to face up to the inevitable explosion of population that resulted, led to an environment that contained more hunger, misery, and danger to the world than before. Again the tide flowed on till the world population rose to the point where it could no longer feed itself by the old primitive methods of agriculture. Even in the United States the resulting change in the environment became painfully apparent.

There have been many forces that helped to encourage the migration from country to city, but chief among them has been the growing demand for food and the resulting revolution in the methods of farming, which, as we saw earlier, crowded so many people off the land and into the city. The slow tide moved almost imperceptibly into the cities, to an environment where the majority of the newcomers were totally unfitted to support themselves and their families.

New York City, the biggest and richest city, is perhaps the most dramatic example of the web of interacting forces that has built up a vicious spiral of decay within the city. The wave of unskilled jobseekers, unable to support themselves, added greatly to the city burden of taxation for welfare, for low cost housing, and for education. At the same time the increasing load of traffic outgrew the capacity of the city streets and highways, bringing traffic to a standstill in some areas. Juvenile delinquency and crime shot upward, calling for higher costs for police protection, courts, and correctional institutions, not to mention the costs to the citizens who were robbed or injured.

As the city became less attractive, those who could afford it moved to the suburbs. It is estimated that between 1950 and 1965 roughly 800,000 middle-income taxpayers moved out of the city, including many who had employed semiskilled or unskilled workers, and that over a period of five years the city lost more than 80,000 jobs in manufacturing. While the city's costs were expanding, it was at the same time losing the taxpayers who were needed to support the growing load, until, in 1966, Mayor John V. Lindsay pointed out that the city was reaching the limit of its ability to raise money. To increase taxes merely resulted in driving more taxpayers and jobs out of the city—in this way transferring to the suburbs the strength needed by the city for its own support.

Many of these suburban emigrants commute daily back to their jobs in the city, which they now aid only indirectly through their state and city taxes. In 1964 roughly 600,000 cars from outside the city moved into the midtown area every day, in this way adding both to the crippling traffic jam and to the pollution of the air. In addition, roughly 200,000 people commuted by rail to the city each weekday, while the railroads, crippled by high taxes and mounting labor costs faced the prospect of cutting down on their commuter service or abandoning it altogether. The city's transit system, swamped by the rush-hour traffic and by high labor costs, was still losing money, unable to grow to meet the traffic needs, and adding heavily to the expense burden of the city.

The needs of the city have expanded so fast that the costs have become astronomical and call for new approaches to a solution. The urbanized surrounding area has grown to take in portions of nine states, a megalopolis extending from Boston to Norfolk, Virginia. The local problems which were once handled by each city or state along the way became so inextricably interdependent and far-reaching that none of the separate governments had either the capacity or the authority to deal with its own problems effectively by itself.

Economically and financially the different areas had become interdependent parts of the same community, whose health required a considerable measure of unified responsibility. It seems clear that, as these supercity areas develop, there will need to be adjustments both to remove the handicap of splintered and overlapping political authority, and also to provide a tax base that can distribute more evenly both the burdens of the overall community and the strength to carry them.

The need for federal help in solving the mass transportation problems of the big cities and for special attention to the locally acute sore-spots of housing, slum clearance, unemployment, education, and others, seems destined to bring the federal government more directly into contact with the solution of local problems. This injection of help and influence from a strong central government into the management of local affairs appears to be essential to meet the growing problems. It highlights again the old problem that is basic to the American form of government and that multiplies with growing size and complexity: that is, how to maintain a form of government that is strong enough to meet the nation's growing needs and, at the same time, to maintain enough local independence and initiative to check the misuse of political power by those who hold it.

It has become obvious that the varying needs of a fast-changing environment are requiring innovations in both the institutions and the management of government. The problem now, in this new environment, is not only to improve the quality of life that it offers to its citizens, but also, especially, within that environment, to produce citizens who will be capable of maintaining that quality in the future.

We have followed some of the steps in the deterioration of a single community under the pressures of growing size and social disorder. Its condition is merely an example of one of the focal points for a long series of chain reactions that spring from changes in the whole human environment. We tend to look at today's conditions and think of remedies in terms of today's environment. In doing this it is important to remember that today's remedies must fit tomorrow's environment, which will be very different from that of today, for the great underlying tide of chain reactions from today, the growing flood of hungry mouths and rebellious spirits, calls for more effective measures.

In attempting to solve his problems, for the first time in human history man has two new forces working in his favor: With his new understanding of the human mind there is the hope that he may learn to discipline his instinct for self-deception, that he may learn to see his problems as a whole and with understanding in his confrontations with his fellow individuals and nations, thus reaching accommodation and cooperation while there is still time. Moreover, science and the unemotional computer may help him to do this, both by example and by helping him to grasp the fantastic extent of the interrelationships that must be brought into workable harmony.

CHAPTER XII

Environment and Human Quality

The development of every human being is controlled by two basic influences, the genetic qualities that he inherits from his parents and the molding of these qualities during the plastic years of growth. This molding is accomplished by the interaction between the inherited personal qualities of the individual and the human and physical influences in his environment. In this interplay of forces, how much is preordained for each individual by the chance mixing of inherited genes, and how much is the result of later molding by environment or intelligence?

With the exception of identical twins, no two people are born with the same genetic makeup, and, except in the case of such twins, it is very difficult to assess the relative influence of heredity and environment. Careful studies have been made of identical twins who have been separated in early childhood and reared under different conditions of environment and educational opportunity, and these have been compared with others who had been brought up together in their own homes.

Such studies indicate that, while there is a limit set by heredity to the mental capacity of any individual, there is a considerable range of achievement within the inherited limits which can be influenced by education and other factors in the environment. While it has not been possible to measure accurately the relative influence of the different environmental factors, the studies suggest that, on the average, roughly three quarters to four fifths of the final result is determined by heredity, while about a fifth to a quarter can be determined by environment, although there may be wide individual variations.

The effects of this environmental influence may start at a very early age. At the University of California Dr. David Krech and his associates for several years carried on studies of the brain development of growing rats, taking baby rats from the same litters and raising them under different controlled conditions. In these experiments the babies in one group would be raised alone in small cages, with a minimum of disturbance or handling. The others were raised in groups, in larger cages, with the stimulation of companionship and play, with exercise wheels, ladders, and other diversions.

Every day these rats were taken from their cages and given a chance to investigate new environments. These experiments showed, with great consistency, that the rats with the more stimulating environment not only developed a larger brain size, chiefly in the cerebral cortex, which controls voluntary action and thought, but that there were also changes in some types of brain cells and in certain biochemical substances which are important in the transmission of nerve impulses. While some students have questioned the assumption that tests on rats can be meaningful for man, there is general agreement that what happens in a rat can and does take place in man.

This test with rats would seem to substantiate the conclusion that environment may play an important part in determining the mental equipment with which a child starts its life, and that when deprived of the stimulation of maternal care and love a child's development may be retarded, physically, mentally, and socially, and that this handicap may persist throughout life. Environmental conditions may also play a key part in setting the pattern of a child's approach to life.

A dog drools saliva when he hears a sound that he has

been trained to associate with food. It is not the sound alone that makes him drool; it is the so-called conditioned reflex response of his nervous system to the imprint left by the earlier experience which associated the sound with food. How many experiences are there which may imprint lasting reflex reactions of this kind in the plastic nervous system of the young child, to build a personality which automatically responds for good or ill to the innumerable experiences of everyday life?

How early do such experiences begin to have their effect? Dr. Justin H. Call, at the University of California Medical School at Los Angeles, made a study of children during their first few days of life, as they were affected by the relationship between mother and child. He believed that the earliest experience of the child in learning to nurse, with help or frustrations from the mother, may affect certain attitudes of the child throughout life, including the capacity for learning. Here we may see the contrast between the child's response to the fulfillment of its basic need for love and care or, by contrast, the distrust and resentment caused by the lack of such fulfillment. This attitude, once formed, may well affect the relationship between mother and child and set a pattern which later extends to affect all personal relationships.

Studies have shown that prolonged separation from the mother and a secure home environment beyond the age of three months and up to about thirty months—and to a lesser extent up to the age of five years—can lead to serious emotional and mental retardation, sometimes lasting for life. Children thus damaged are less equipped to bring their own children up properly, thereby continuing the vicious circle.

The child's earliest experiences play a basic role in preparing the mind for future development. This comes about through a series of steps, each one preparing the mind for the next. Recognition of the sight and touch of things paves the way for learning the more complicated qualities of shape or color, hardness or softness. Later, the physical qualities will be associated with the sounds of the voice, and through contacts with elders comes the ability to distinguish between sounds as a first step toward recognizing words and concepts.

These steps in the habits of recognition and association, each step based on already established knowledge, play a big part in the preparation for reading, for the handling of mental concepts, and for reasoning. The lack of such stimulating preparatory experience may be an irreversible handicap to the slum child entering school, in competition with more experienced children, and this becomes apparent when he does not learn to read properly in the early grades. Tests in some of the schools in New York's Harlem showed third-grade pupils averaging a year below grade level in academic performance. Three years later, in the sixth grade, the average had dropped to nearly two years below grade level. As the child falls further behind and loses self-confidence, his I.Q. may actually decline, and this failure can have a serious psychological effect and be an important cause of school dropouts.

While there are no final answers yet, recent investigations suggest very strongly that deprivation of normal experience during the early months of a young child's life can slow up the development of intelligence and that this effect may be permanent. Professor J. McV. Hunt, one of the pioneer investigators in this field, has suggested that perhaps 20% of a child's basic acquired abilities are developed within the first twelve months and about half of them before the age of four years.

Studies of children raised in institutions with little personal attention beyond their physical needs, when compared with children raised under more normal conditions, seem to bear out the finding that environment during the earliest years of life can have an important bearing on the development of the child.

Concerning the development of personality, Berelson and Steiner find that "the state of current knowledge is often contradictory and inconclusive" owing to the difficulty of applying scientific measurements and to the great complexity of the subject, but they conclude, "Stimulation and contact—physical, mental, and social—are necessary for normal human development (i.e., development into what the members of the society would consider a human being)." Considering the infinite variety of gradations in experience of the growing child this statement must obviously receive a rather elastic interpretation. It does express the principle that love and attention, wherever they may be experienced, play a very important part in the early life of the young child.

In a study at the Albert Einstein College of Medicine under a grant from the National Institutes of Health a group of doctors found that children with emotional problems, such as parents feuding at home, had trouble learning to read.

This influence from the home environment carries forward in a sort of chain reaction to affect the child's later development. Professor and Mrs. Sheldon Glueck, working as a team at Harvard University, made an exhaustive study of juvenile delinquency and developed a prediction scale based on five different factors in the home, giving each factor a weight, or score, based on its indicated importance as a contributor toward the development of juvenile delinquency.

These factors were:

		Weighted effect toward failure
1)	Discipline by Father—	
	a—Overstrict or erratic	71.8
	b—Lax	59.8
	c—Firm but kindly	9.3
2)	Supervision by Mother	
	a—Unsuitable	83.2
	b—Fair	57.5
	c—Close or suitable	9.9
3)	Affection for Father	
	a—Indifferent or hostile	75.9
	b—Warm	33.8
4)	Affection for Mother	
	a—Indifferent or hostile	86.2
	b—Warm	43.1
5)	Cohesiveness of Family	
	a—Unintegrated	91.8
	b—Some cohesion	61.3
	c—Cohesive	10.8

Studies by the New York City Youth Board over a period of four years, based on estimates of individual family relationships by trained workers, and using the above scale, showed the following results:

Weighted Failure Score	Chances of Delinquency	Chances of Non-delinquency
Under 200	8.2	91.8
200-249	37.0	63.0
250-299	63.5	36.5
300 and up	89.0	10.8

Ten years after this study was initiated, the Youth Board reported results for two schools in a high-delinquency neighborhood. Here the forecasts for delinquency were 85% accurate and for nondelinquency the accuracy was 95%.

Actually a large proportion of the delinquent children came from homes where there was no father present, but over a four year period the results conformed fairly closely with the ratings earned by the pupils in their first school year. This would seem incontrovertible evidence of the key importance of the home in the development of human quality. But where does the home begin?

How many of today's parents are equipped to give their children a fair start? Many of these parents, and their parents before them, got their start in homes broken by war and the great depression of the 1930's. Many have never seen a successful home. All are living today in a strange new environment subject to pressures and temptations that, in some degree at least, are new to human experience. Their children escape from parental supervision by way of the automobile and by the pressures of the gang spirit of revolt against the authority that restrains them.

The ability of the home to function must be found in the quality, or spirit, of the community, which embodies many homes and which, by its tone, influences both the parents and the children who make the homes. By the test of spreading juvenile delinquency, neither the average home nor the community is providing an adequate environment for developing the growing youth who must manage the world's problems tomorrow. For all our exploding population, the growth of juvenile delinquency and crime is exploding even faster.

Juvenile delinquency, rioting, and destructive violence have appeared in all technical societies, whether Anglo-Saxon, Latin, Japanese, or Russian. They have been especially troublesome in slum environments. Even among college students from good homes, presumably our best material for citizens of the future, preparing to qualify for leadership, riots have been violent and destructive. The exploding use of narcotics and psychotoxic drugs is wrecking young lives at all social levels.

Society has always had its revolts against authority, but today's riots and delinquency have taken on a new appearance. In the F.B.I. report for 1963, J. Edgar Hoover tells of a year's total of more than two-and-a-half million serious crimes in the United States. This means one serious crime every fifteen seconds on the average, day and night, throughout the year, representing an increase of 40% for the five years of 1958 to 1963. This was five times faster than the increase in the number of people, and the greatest rise was among the teen-agers. This rise has continued and the tendency has been worldwide.

There are obviously many causes that contributed to this startling rise, but one fact seems especially significant. The crime rate in the bigger cities was much higher than for the smaller ones, for the period of the report. This does not mean just an increase in numbers; it is the *rate*, or number for each 1,000 people. In cities with a population over a quarter million, the rate was seven times that in the surrounding suburban areas and fifteen times that of the rural areas. In cities with over a million people, the rate jumped to four times that for all other cities and nineteen times that of the rural areas. Since this report the rate has tended to rise in the suburbs compared to the cities, but the trouble apparently originated in the cities.

It was estimated that the cost of this crime came to at least $27 billion a year.

The value of a human life cannot be estimated, but this crime total included 8,500 murders, approximately one every hour, day and night, throughout the year; 16,400 forcible rapes, nearly two every hour; and 147,800 aggravated assaults. In the course of combatting these crimes fifty-five policemen were murdered in 1963 and 17,693 were assaulted.

When discontent and organized crime reach the point of open and violent defiance of the law and the murder of its agents, it is time for the community to examine itself, to seek to learn why its attempts at self-government have fallen down, and how it can remedy the condition.

If we compare the crime rate in different cities of comparable size we get some very significant results. Why, for example, did the rate of serious crime in New York City rise by 13% in the three years from 1960 to 1963 while the rate in Chicago rose 31%, nearly 2½ times as much, in the same period? Why did the rate in Cincinnati, with its half million citizens, rise by 86% while that in nearby Columbus, of comparable size, actually dropped by 20%? Why did the rate for Atlanta's half million rise by 73%, while that of Phoenix, of about the same size, dropped by 17%? These variations might be partly explained by differences in basic criteria, but their size suggests that they go deeper. The record indicates that they lie at least partly within the control of the individual city. Chicago, once known as the crime capital of the world, gave proof of this when it engaged a new police chief, Orlando Wilson, who radically reorganized the police force, and reversed its crime rate from a steep rise to a 3% drop in 1963, a 5% drop in 1964, and 12% in 1965.

The opinion has been widely expressed by judges, police commissioners, and other authorities on the subject, that the first need is to enforce respect for the law, and that this is hampered by flaws in the structure and interpretation of the law as it now exists. Blame has been placed on our whole system of criminal justice, including legal technicalities which can make it impossible even to convict a person caught in the act.

Judge Robert Gardner of the Superior Court, Orange

County, California, has criticized the tendency in juvenile courts to treat all delinquents under eighteen as merely problem children regardless of the seriousness of their crimes. Knowing this, the "wise juvie" becomes a repeater, practically immune to punishment, and often a hardened criminal before he reaches the age of adult responsibility at 18. This is an injustice both to the youth and the community that he preys on. It would seem time to emphasize that civil liberties depend in the first place on civil responsibility and that when the two come into conflict, the protection of the community comes first.

While law enforcement is an essential start toward community health, the real cure must lie deeper, in the community's way of life and in the finding of new approaches to the basic values that have been altered or destroyed by science, urbanization, and exploding populations.

There is deep significance in the conclusions of some students of juvenile delinquency that the most effective cure for delinquency is marriage to a good girl. While the children-to-be of such a marriage might reasonably ask for some advance guarantee of responsibility and opportunity from their future parents, this experience does strongly suggest that with no change in the outside environment, the delinquent is reformed by finding a relationship that was lacking in his own home. In his shared love he finds life's most enriching and enlightening experience and with it the incentive and the responsibility to play a man's part. His final success will still depend, not only on his environment, but also largely on his own abilities, whose sources we have already considered.

The nation is filled with millions of good homes with splendid parents and children, but the problems of the average home have radically changed. In 1790, at its birth, our young nation had a population of nearly four million people who lived chiefly on the land; 95% of them lived in the country, most of them on farms. By 1950 the farm population had dropped to about 15%. Then, in just twelve years, it dropped to only 7.7%. These figures can't be compared exactly with those for 1790, owing to changing definitions of urban and rural, but they show the dramatic change that has taken place in the environment that must build the oncoming generations.

On the farm, the family worked as a team, sharing common responsibilities. Each one experienced the direct connection between the quality of his contribution and the welfare of all. Daily challenges tested the resourcefulness and stamina of the team. The family prospered or went hungry as its own abilities mastered or failed to meet these tests. Each one experienced the inborn satisfaction of using his own skill and strength to produce a finished result that was useful to himself and the others. It was a hard way of life, with many failures, and a short life span for the average lot. On the average, the strongest and ablest survived, and these were the ones selected by nature's immemorial method to pass on their inheritance to the next generation. With that inheritance went a love and understanding of the land.

Certainly the city dweller of today has many advantages over the farm family of only a few years ago, but as a place for the rearing of children, who are to be the parents of future children, the city home has lost some basic values. It permits a more exciting and stimulating life, but it doesn't meet some of the deepest human needs. The problems and tensions of employment, or the search for employment, under modern industrial conditions, are perhaps unavoidable, but the closing of the farm frontier means more than just the loss of the pool of unskilled jobs; it means changing a nation's way of life, and it calls for the finding of values and qualities in the new life to replace the old ones that have been lost.

The psychological effects of working as a numbered cog in an impersonal machine may be only subconsciously felt. Many people can no doubt adjust to it happily, not as a way of life, but as a part of life that is endured because it brings the means for living. Its value is measured chiefly in money, rather than in the satisfactions offered by the work itself. The record of industrial labor disputes does not suggest that the world's highest material standard of living has produced a really satisfying kind of life.

What can an industrial economy offer to compensate for its drawbacks? Education, for those who are interested to use it, can open a new world of interests and rewards beyond the much publicized ability to make money. It can be one helpful answer to the growing problem of boredom through sterile leisure.

Education alone is not enough. Without motivation or incentive for its effective use, education can be as futile and disturbing as too much leisure. The problem goes deeper than education, down to the incentives and inner motivations that condition the development of a useful citizen. We can recognize some of the things that have been lost in the modern depersonalized urban environment—the weakened influence of home, community, tradition, and education; but there is still a lot to be learned about the social *malaise* that seeps in to take their place.

CHAPTER XIII

Environment and Motivation

We have discussed some of our urban problems, looking chiefly at the symptoms. What can we learn about the deep underlying causes, the inner motivations that make people act as they do in response to urban conditions?

Dr. Edward T. Hall, Professor of Anthropology at Northwestern University, has made a significant study of human motivation and action under the crowded conditions of a big city. Referring to the study by Glazier and Moynihan, reported in their book *Beyond the Melting Pot,* he points out that there is actually no melting pot, as we ordinarily think of it, in the American cities, since the major ethnic groups "maintain distinct identities for several generations." He states further that our housing and city-planning programs seldom take these differences into account and that one of the most critical needs in city planning is for principles of design that will maintain a continuing sense of ethnic identification together with a proper amount of involvement.

Referring to the disadvantaged Negro as a specific example, Dr. Hall makes the point that some cultural problems of the Negro, while they may be sharpened by prejudice, are not the same as prejudice. They "lie at the core of the human situation, and they are as old as man." It will help to gain perspective on this problem if we think of the original structure of human society. In Chapter IV (page 34) we noted the estimate that a human family, living by hunting and food-gathering, requires from ten to fifty square miles of land for its support; early man was thus limited to living in very small, well-separated groups which must necessarily reject any addition to their numbers. This was true for many hundreds of thousands of years during the time when human culture was developing.

In Chapter IV (page 37) we noted also Professor Mumford's estimate of the important role that family and tribal influence and tradition played in maintaining social structure and order. He pointed out that when different cultural groups were crowded together in the early cities the cultural disciplines tended to disintegrate into group hostility and disorder.

What goes on within the human personality to bring about this mass disintegration? Crowding does play an important part, but Professor Hall points out that the key factor seems to be the crowding together of different types of culture. Among many examples of cultural difference he mentions the "polychronic" personality of the southern European who enjoys much talk and engagement in a variety of interests at the same time. The "monochronic" northern European, on the other hand, tends to stick to one thing at a time and to be much disturbed by too much involvement with the polychronic approach. The obvious differences in Japanese or Arab and Western personalities and ways of living—without any connotation of better or worse—can still become very difficult under crowded conditions and can have important effects on problems of finding jobs or of social harmony.

Many kinds of tests on the psychological and physiological effects of crowding are not possible with humans, but tests with animals give some very significant results. At the Penrose Laboratory of the Philadelphia Zoo, pathologists H. L. Ratcliffe and R. L. Snyder, quoted in Hall, reported recently on a study of the causes of death of 16,000 birds and mammals over a period of twenty-five years. This showed that many kinds of animals suffer stress from overcrowding, and they are affected by the same diseases as man: high blood pressure, heart and circulatory diseases, even when receiving a low-fat diet.

These are symptoms. What goes on within the animal to cause the symptoms? Professor Hall uses the word "exocrinology" to denote the influence that external factors may exert on the functioning of the endocrine system, which so largely governs the physiological and psychological functions. Dr. Hans Selye has demonstrated that animals which are subjected to repeated stress can die of shock if the continuing demands for fresh energy to meet the stress exhaust the supply of blood sugar. The stress of crowding leads to enlargement of the adrenal glands.

We have already discussed (Chapter VI, page 56) a study by Dr. John B. Calhoun on crowding in laboratory mice. Hall refers to another study by Calhoun in which he placed five pregnant wild Norway rats in an outdoor pen that covered a quarter of an acre. During a test period of twenty-eight months these rats received plenty of food, with no pressure from predators. The resulting offspring never exceeded 200 and finally stabilized at 150. These rats did not scatter at random around the pen. They organized themselves into separate colonies of twelve rats each. Each colony had its own territory and its own normal social structure and living pattern. Headed by a dominant male, the colony comprised a hierarchy of subordinate males and females which followed the normal patterns of courting, mating, nest building, and caring for the young. This group size appeared to be the largest number that could live harmoniously in a natural group, and even with this organization there was so much fighting as to disrupt the care of the young, only a few of which survived.

At their normal rate of reproduction the five females which mothered this experiment could have produced a colony of 50,000 young during the period of the test, in contrast to the 150 that actually survived in the undivided pen. Experience has shown that the full 50,000 could be kept alive and healthy in the same quarter-acre space if they were housed in small cages. Boxed so that they cannot see each other the numbers can be increased indefinitely. The animals had evolved with instincts which protected them against such an increase.

Following this experiment Calhoun conducted further tests to learn the effects of crowding on social organization and individual condition. He found that crowding beyond a certain density led to what he called a "behavioral sink," in which social organization broke down and all forms of pathology were aggravated, including disruption of nest building, courting, sex behavior, and reproduction. Autopsied rats showed serious physiological effects as well.

An interesting point was brought out in these tests: crowding alone was not the critical factor which brought on the "sink" condition. Increased activity, which led to greater interaction and stress, brought on the breaking point at a lower level of density. Such activity was induced in the test rats by arranging their communal feed hoppers so that they had to spend more time in getting their food, thus bringing the males of the different groups into more frequent contact, with more resultant fighting and scuffling.

When the sink developed, the mortality among the female rats rose to three-and-one-half times that of the males. Less care was taken of the nests, and only one fourth of the young survived to weaning time, many being eaten by the overactive males. Pan-sexuality and sadism became endemic. There was much tail biting among the males. Tumors and other disorders appeared in the reproductive organs of the females. Kidneys, adrenals, and livers were enlarged or diseased.

Calhoun concluded that even the hardy rat cannot tolerate

disorder and that, like man, he needs some time to be alone. Crowding, alone, might not be enough to produce these symptoms, but it does disrupt important social functions and leads to disorganization and ultimately to collapse.

Professor Hall comments that when a sink develops in a city, its management is beyond the normal capacities of the city law-enforcement agencies, and that even if it were possible to abolish all prejudice and discrimination in the city, the lower class Negro would still be under extreme stress because of the cultural differences between himself and the dominant middle-class white in a completely foreign environment. Considering the large numbers of Negroes who have successfully moved across to the status of the middle-class whites, it seems especially significant that, in the riots of 1967, these successful Negroes suffered from the violence and ill will of the rioters along with the whites. Cultural difference appeared to be as imporant as color.

Dr. Hall points out that it is the cumulative effect of crowding which leads to these unhappy sink conditions and that in some ways they resemble the cancer that comes from cigarette smoking—they do not appear until after the stress has done its internal damage, and they threaten to make the big cities ungovernable. But he asserts that, rather than letting the sink destroy the city, it is possible through proper design features to reduce the crowding without destroying the ethnic enclave. It is obviously possible also to reduce some of the causes of environmental stress.

The pollution of city air and city streets can at least be reduced. The depersonalization that builds the lonely crowds of a big city can also be ameliorated, as Mayor Lindsay of New York demonstrated in the summer of 1967. With conditions as potentially inflammable as in any of the big cities, his programs of entertainment in the parks, together with his frequent personal visits to the slum sections of the city, undoubtedly did their share to reduce the tensions of the summer, and New York City thus suffered much less rioting than some other cities.

Open spaces for city parks play a very important part, and the more distant open spaces that are available for public recreation also play a vital role. The report of the Outdoor Recreation Resources Review Commission in 1962 brought out the fact that in the ten years from 1950 to 1960 the use of the recreational areas of the national parks and forests and of the state parks more than doubled and that the total visits to recreation areas, including local parks, in 1960, came to 532 million day visits and 52 million overnight visits. On the basis of the present growth rate it was estimated that by the year 2000 the participation in outdoor recreation would nearly triple. It was pointed out that the present areas for outdoor recreation are far from adequate to meet the needs which are basically important to the physical and emotional health of millions of people.

With 283 million acres of publicly owned land listed as available for recreational use, it might seem that the nation was well supplied. But much of this is inaccessible to the people who need it most. Only one twenty-fifth of it is in the Northeast, where a quarter of all the people live. Most of the rest is in the West, including Alaska, where it is inaccessible to many of the city dwellers who need it most. Much of it is not adapted for the needed uses.

Of all the recreational activities, driving for pleasure and swimming are listed as the most popular. Next come walking for pleasure and playing outdoor games. Well below these are sight-seeing, picnicking, fishing, bicycling, watching outdoor sports, boating, taking nature walks, hunting, camping, horseback-riding, water-skiing, hiking, and attending outdoor concerts, in descending order. These activities were estimated to have accounted for more than four-and-one-third billion occasions of participation in 1960, with twelve-and-a-half billion expected by the year 2000.

Many of these activities have their own special requirements: adequate roads, clean water and shorelines, pathways, playing areas, and wildlife cover.

For the national parks and other less accessible areas there are needs for overnight accommodations with proper supervision and sanitation. Large appropriations are needed to acquire more river and beach lands before they are all gone. Consumer spending for outdoor recreation in 1960 was estimated at about $20 billion. Through taxes and users' fees this huge business can be made to support much of the needed acquisition and improvement.

The study committee pointed out that even in the heavily urbanized areas there were many opportunities for open space for recreation. Housing developments can be built in clusters with surrounding open space and trees. Small areas of woods, ponds, and streams offer space for paths and picnic spots. Foot and bicycle paths along highway rights of way and high tension lines offer other possibilities.

Beauty in the environment makes an irreplaceable contribution to the flowering of the human spirit and imagination— qualities which, on the other hand, are blighted by ugliness and pollution. Too much of economic development has been

associated with the defilement of the air, water, and land-
scape. Today human art is faced with the challenge to replace
the nation's man-made ugliness with the lift to the spirit that
only beauty can give.

Hungry people crowd into cities, concentrating frustration,
despair, and alienation into tightly packed explosive mixtures.
Scientists, engineers, and politicians labor to ameliorate the
resulting symptoms, attacking the obvious physical problems.
But the key to success would appear to lie in the search for a
clearer understanding of the forces that shape human motivation. The inescapable prerequisite is to limit the rising flood
of hungry mouths that mulitiply the problems.

The decade of the 1960's has seen the world community
waking to both the dangers and the possibilities in its new environment and testing new approaches that are filled with
both great dangers and great hopes. The "Great Society" program, in spite of the blind chain reactions that it will set in
motion, is at least an attempt to coordinate the best of human
knowledge into effective action. The need now is for human
wisdom to chart the way to success—to build an environment
where men and women can develop and carry forward the
motivations for civilized living.

CHAPTER XIV

Government and Individual
Rights

Since earliest recorded history, man has fought, thought,
and experimented in the effort to devise some orderly system
for governing his relations with his fellow man. There is no
record of any system that has been permanently successful
nor of any that could succeed under all conditions of size, education, or economic and social circumstance. As a nation
grows and develops, altering the environment of its citizens,
human nature reacts in its own characteristic ways in response to the changes.

The basic dilemma of government is to find a workable
balance between the freedom for self-government, on the one
hand, and the strength for effective government on the other
—and always to maintain a defense against the basic human

instinct to abuse power, or freedom, once it has been achieved.

Today we see the world divided between the two basic ideologies, one believing that the individual cannot be trusted with freedom, that he is the servant of the state, to be molded and directed by the rulers of the state for the benefit of the community as a whole; on the other side we see the various forms of democratic government, dedicated to the freedom of the individual, but in many cases finding it increasingly difficult to protect the welfare of the community against the irresponsible use of this freedom by its many individuals. With these governments the basic problem seems to be to build and maintain in the voting citizens the qualities and the standards of responsibility that are necessary to govern themselves in freedom. This, in turn, calls for an environment that can produce such qualities and protect them. Between these two main ideas of government we see the many nations that are searching for some form that can succeed under their own special conditions of illiteracy, poverty, social unrest, and backgrounds of instability.

The Constitution of the United States is an attempt to establish the principles under which a favorable environment for democracy might be preserved, using the same principle of checks and balances that we have seen in the natural community. James Madison, one of its creators, said of it: "Every word of [the Constitution] decides a question between power and liberty." In the words of the late President Kennedy, "It is the best system yet devised, but we have to make it work." To make any democratic form of government work requires more than a good constitution and good laws. It requires citizens with the education to understand the issues and the problems, and the standards and motivations to accept the necessary responsibilities.

Woodrow Wilson said, "The only absolute safeguards of a constitutional system . . . lie in the character, the independence, the resolution, the right purpose of the men who vote and who choose the public servants of whom the Government is to consist. . . . The men of whom it consists will be no better than the men who choose them."

The United States has its good Constitution and yet its problems of maintaining social and economic stability, public order, and respect for law appear to be steadily growing more acute. To meet these problems the government, with consistently strong support from the electorate, has taken steps which steadily and increasingly encroach on personal freedom, private enterprise, and private property. These are the values which have, in the past, promoted incentive, initiative, and responsibility for good citizenship—the values for which the nation was founded—and yet they have led to problems which threaten their own existence. Some change in the environment has evidently evoked a force stronger than law and constitution.

Dr. Robert M. MacIver has pointed out that in every community there is a force, or authority, that is greater than the authority of government; this is the consensus of the community opinion. Its force was shown clearly in the enactment and later breakdown and repeal of the Volstead Act, which sought to impose prohibition on the nation in the 1920's. Congress passed the law, but experience soon proved that the community would not support what it considered unreasonable interference with individual freedom, and, against this consensus, even the police power of the nation could not enforce the law.

It is perhaps hard to realize that this vast, intangible, yet explosive force of public opinion is made up of over 100 million separate individual reactions (there were 110 million U.S. citizens of voting age in 1962). These reactions represent numberless differences and conflicts of personal interest and prejudice: the government employee who wants to hold his job; the union leader seeking benefits for his union and himself; the industrialist whose business, together with its employees and stockholders, will sink or swim on the outcome of a vote to protect his products from foreign competition.

In this environment there are two major forces. There is the great mass of voters, each tending to see today's conditions from the narrow viewpoint of his own experience and to judge them from the bias of his own interest. There are also the responsible leaders whose job it is to see the community, not as it appears on the surface today, but to look beneath the surface at the great intangible stream of chain reactions that are set in motion by the conditions of today, to build entirely new conditions for tomorrow. The success of human society in another year, or ten years, will depend in large measure on the foundation that is being laid in today's environment. The foundation is built by the quality of the minds that its education turns out, the quality of the opportunity that it offers to these minds, and the quality of the motivation that its homes and traditions instill in those minds.

There are many chain reactions in progress today that foretell the likelihood of new approaches by government in the not distant future, but small evidence of consensus on how the approaches can be made. There is still to be found some adequate solution for the narrowing of the American frontier of opportunity and for the growing deterioration of the urban environment. For each problem, enormously costly programs of improvement are proposed, and each may be within the limits of what the whole society can afford, but, lumped together, all of these programs take on astronomical proportions. Entirely aside from the question of finding the money, the problem of finding and training leaders, and administering an adequate bureaucracy to handle the money and the projects, calls for superhuman qualities. The voting power inherent within such a special interest group of public officials foreshadows a chain reaction toward a new concentration of power.

The monopoly powers of huge labor unions, with their special legal privileges, have given the worker much needed help in attaining equality of opportunity, but now the power has grown to the point where it threatens the welfare of the whole society. The problem is still to discover how to enforce responsible use of that power without putting dangerous political power in the hands of government.

The narrowing of the frontier of opportunity has made necessary a growing amount of government assistance for welfare and aggravated the question of human rights. Every dollar of assistance comes out of the pocket of the taxpayer, either today or in the future.

What, for example, are the rights of the tenant farmer, evicted from his home in the South? He arrives in New York, helpless and dependent on the assistance of a financially hard pressed city. What are the responsibilities of this struggling city for the housing and support of 100,000 strangers? What are their rights to demand support? What are the responsibilities of the states, the federal government and the society which unwittingly tolerated the conditions that caused their plight? What are the rights of the taxpayers who must suffer for their benefit?

The answer would seem to be that rights can have meaning only through the exercise of responsibility by a society that is strong enough and orderly enough to uphold and enforce them. The welfare of the society is the cornerstone of individual rights.

The United States has evolved from a society of free and independent citizens into a community of inescapably interdependent members of a single complex machine. The economic system that creates the nation's jobs is fueled to an important degree by government distribution of buying power that is taxed from the pockets of its citizens. Every member of the community is dependent, in greater or lesser degree, on the taxes drawn from other people for his support. The welfare of the community depends on maintaining a workable balance between the burdens and the benefits of this system of redistributing wealth. The right of a person to receive benefits can exist only so long as the community is able to carry the burden of the payment. The problem of social and political stability may come at the point when the mass vote of the beneficiaries overwhelms the power of the society to support them. We see some foretaste of this in the huge build-up of urban needs for housing, education, welfare, transportation, pollution control, and public order.

Society places many restrictions on individual freedoms. It controls traffic on the highways, prohibits the distribution of dangerous drugs, and so on, but there is one responsibility that has not been adequately faced. Many parents on relief have no prospect of being able to support more children or give them an adequate upbringing. In a study by the New York City Youth Board in 1957 it was brought out that the multiproblem families in the city had, on the average, four times as many children as the average for the city as a whole, that two thirds of these families had six or more children, and that more than half of them were totally dependent on public assistance.

This situation brings up some interesting questions of rights and responsibilities. In such large families a working mother cannot give proper attention to the growing children. Each new, and often unwanted child thus becomes a handicap or a calamity to the older children and, as the Glueck study showed (Chapter XII, page 102), a potential candidate for juvenile delinquency. Such a child might well ask for the protection of his right not to be born. His brothers and sisters might ask for the protection of their right to a decent family life. The community assumes the responsibility to give these children a good start in life, but, in assuming this responsibility, does it also have the right to place a limit on the right of the parents to continue adding new children to the load on society? Do the other members of the community have a right to be protected against such irresponsible disregard of the public welfare?

Between the years 1940 and 1961 the number of illegitimate births in the United States rose from 89,500 to 240,200, an increase of two-and-a-half in twenty years, and the number continues to grow. Such births add far more than their proportionate share to the burden of the welfare rolls and the blight of juvenile delinquency. It has been estimated that between 40% and 45% of the children on Aid to Dependent

Children relief in Cook County, Illinois, are illegitimate. To protect all its members and its own quality it is important for the community to control more effectively the irresponsible parenthood that imposes such burdens on the lives of others, just as it imposes speed laws to protect lives on the highway. It has been estimated that in Puerto Rico one woman in every six of childbearing age has been sterilized, usually after having as many children as desired.

There are no definitive figures, but estimates on illegal abortions range from 1,000,000 to 1,200,000 in the United States each year, with resulting deaths of about 10,000 women. This seems a high price to pay for what many doctors feel to be antiquated laws on the subject. Perhaps the first right to be considered here is the right of an unborn child who, there is reason to believe, bears a serious and permanent defect. If such a defect is disclosed by x-ray before birth, the child might be spared a life of helpless misery by an abortion. But, unless the mother's safety is in danger, an abortion is generally forbidden in most of the states, on pain of years in prison for the physician. But how about the safety of the child? Here is a living spark that has never known consciousness as we know it in the outside world, a spark that can never have an adequate body to make a complete life, but, unless the mother's life is at stake, the law condemns this partly formed being to a life of helpless misery. The cost in needless tragedy for the child and its parents can't be measured. The resulting burden on the other children and parents of the community also has its elements of tragedy which can be partly estimated in the cost of lifelong institutional care that is needed for many such defective children.

The world has been much concerned over the religious belief that any artificial interference with the origins of human life is contrary to natural law. Under this belief, the effective control of human reproduction has been forbidden to many millions of people. Since such prohibition has a bearing on the welfare of the people of the entire world, it becomes pertinent to ask: What is natural law? Through the ages of human experience man has learned that certain principles of action work for the highest development and welfare of the individual and the community. Such principles might be considered as natural law. Some of these laws can be demonstrated fairly clearly. We have seen that any population which multiplies beyond the carrying capacity of its environment inevitably brings onto itself the forces of environmental resistance. This will eventually, and harshly, bring the multiplication back toward a balance with, or below that of the original carrying capacity. We see that law in action very clearly today. We see it in the thousands of daily deaths from starvation in scattered parts of the world. We see it in the exploding psychological problems, in the growing tensions from population pressures throughout the world, and in the simple arithmetic that shows the fast approaching limits of space, food production, and international tempers.

The new conditions of today's environment impose the requirement that the human birth rate be brought into better balance with the modern death rate. Under these conditions the rather rarefied argument for natural law against artificial control comes into direct confrontation with the inescapable natural law governing the relationship between numbers and carrying capacity. It would seem wise to take a new look at the confrontation between dogma and the welfare of mankind. Natural law threatens to achieve a new balance by magnifying the death rate if human law does not forestall it by reducing the birth rate.

The American melting pot has made great strides toward ameliorating racial and religious prejudice between groups that were hostile in their native lands. But, as swarming populations increase the tensions of competition for food and resources, the old instincts of group hostility come to the fore again. This challenge seems likely to become a major test of man's ability to govern himself in peace. The world has seen it flare up in Hitler's gas furnaces; in the conflagration of mutual mass slaughter between Moslem and Hindu when India first gained its independence; between Communist and non-Communist in Indonesia; and between Arab and Jew in the Near East. It appears in the nationalistic spirit of every nation and among competing groups in every nation.

The cleavage between white and nonwhite skins is perhaps the most obvious and widespread and the most important to solve. While many influences have tended to intensify the prejudices between black and white, the geneticist insists that there is actually little, if any genetic difference in the inherent mental capacities of the different racial groups. All are of the same species, *Homo sapiens*. In the long aeons of evolutionary development, interbreeding, and mixing of genetic qualities, all have shared the same blood types, some of which cannot be safely mixed in blood transfusions. It is the type of blood, not the color, that determines the difference. A white man who inherits blood type A cannot tolerate a transfusion from a white man who has blood type B, but he can be helped by blood type A from a Negro. All draw their genetic qualities from the same pool of human inheritance.

Dr. Ernst Mayr has pointed out that, although it is possible for mental differences to exist, there is no mental trait for which a clear-cut racial difference has been established. The differences between members of a single race are usually larger than the differences between races. Dr. James B. Conant has pointed out that community and family background play an important part in determining scholastic aptitude and that, in scholastic aptitude tests, some Negroes will always score better than most whites while some whites will always score lower than most Negroes.

Thus, the bias and prejudice which have condemned the Negro to both inferior education and lessened economic opportunity is self-defeating. It not only deprives the community of great potential abilities and lays on it a heavy burden of welfare costs, it also confines the Negro to the lower, less-educated levels of society, where his birth rate is much higher than that of his educated Negro brother. Much emphasis is rightly laid on social justice in this situation, and it is easy to forget that social sanity and the validity of the U.S. Constitution are also involved. The segregationist who so insistently proclaims his own rights of free choice fails to recognize that his rights rest on exactly the same foundation of law as the rights of his colored neighbor and that the rights of neither are safe until this truth is upheld.

Government, the ordering of relationships in the human society, appears to be based on the same principles of balanced forces that we saw earlier in the natural community. Constitutional principles and laws to implement them—these supply the rules of the game, but they mean little unless the players accept them. This is true even in the autocracies where unending turmoil highlights the search for balance between governor and governed. In a democracy the balance is much more fragile and more dependent on the conditions of its environment. The Great Society program of the 1960's represents a huge research project, seeking to learn and to understand the requirements of an environment that can produce a citizenry capable of self-government.

It is probably fair to say that free enterprise, as it was known in the last century, destroyed itself through its own inherent weaknesses. But free enterprise supplied the incentives that sustained America's growth. The move toward a welfare state may appear necessary for the preservation of social stability for the present, but one must ask what chain reactions does it set in motion? What incentives does it offer for human growth? Which way will it tip the balance between human instinct and human intelligence?

Section III

TOMORROW

CHAPTER XV

International Relations

For each one of us our relationship to our environment has two sides. First there is the environment that touches us directly—our home, our community, our government, our country. It is easy to think of this surrounding environment as the only one that really matters, but beyond this there is the other, less visible international environment which, in the years ahead, threatens to affect our lives with even greater force.

This environment is made up of more than three billion people whose thoughts and understanding are separated by many barriers—thousands of languages and dialects that are mutually unintelligible; many different scales of value and ways of thinking about them; many different backgrounds of culture, superstitions, and religious beliefs; high education and blank illiteracy; overflowing wealth and hopeless starvation; raw national pride; conflicting national interests and inherited national hatreds sharpened by centuries of migration, aggression, and conquest.

On the average, for all their confrontations, these diverse groups have lived in their own different worlds where they had room to go their separate ways, build their own cultures, and make their own mistakes. Now, in the course of just a few years, overcrowding and the mobility given by science have forced these separate worlds together so that, however unwillingly, they have become inseparable parts of the same one world. Today the environment of every living person extends around the globe, and the survival of each is tied in with the thoughts and actions of other people on the opposite sides of the earth. The populations of many of the poorer nations are swelling beyond the capacity of their lands to feed them. Their mistakes become their neighbors' headaches, and they become dangerous pawns in the confrontations between the stronger powers.

The world problem is how to bring more order into this

chaos of conflicting ambitions, suspicions, and emotions before some spark lights a new world conflagration. Each nation is naturally most concerned with its own pressing problems, but in the end these depend on man's ability to keep his international relations under control. In this situation there appear to be three chief points of pressure: International political antagonisms and distrust hamper every effort at achieving order; hunger and desperation threaten those nations which, overfilled and underfed, are falling behind in the race between food production and population growth; then, there are the economic pressures on those underdeveloped nations which, in spite of foreign aid, have been falling behind in the race to stand on their own economic feet. These problems all seem destined to intensify until the population problem can be mastered.

In the search for order the United Nations offers the world's best hope. With all its problems and failures, it has given the nations a chance to meet and understand each other's problems, to substitute words for blows, and to cooperate on efforts for peace and progress. But the U.N. is only the machinery. To make it work requires the rebuilding of confidence that was shattered by two world wars and the clash of ideologies.

Old leaders depart. New leaders and new experience breed new ideas and can mellow the national policies of both Communist and democratic governments. Certainly every nation still needs to learn more about how best to govern itself in the new world environment. But until the U.N. can build effective power to keep the peace under law; the leaders of the so-called great nations have much of the responsibility for the fate of the world resting on their shoulders.

In this situation the first need is to judge wisely on the relationship between the two great ideologies, to assess the announced Communist aim for world revolution. We see the splintering of the monolithic Communist structure and the tendency of some Communist governments to turn their attention inward on their own problems and away from world revolution. We agree that any nation has a right to experiment with its own form of government, but international sanity requires that no nation should attempt to impose its form of government on another by either force or subversion.

In the absence of effective U.N. power to uphold the peace, what is the responsibility of a great nation to take steps for its own protection? Under the so-called nuclear umbrella of the United States, many nations feel relieved of anxiety about the danger of open Communist attack, but the holder of the umbrella becomes the target of attack from two sides: It is the obstacle that must be overcome by those who still harbor visions of world revolution; it is also the target of criticism from its own beneficiaries who, being safely insulated from the enmity of the revolutionaries, see no need for concern.

What are the responsibilities of the government which holds the umbrella for the protection of its own people? With some differences in detail, this is a dilemma that is as old as civilization. We can look back over 10,000 years to the broken walls of Jericho or a mere 2,500 years to the massive walls of Babylon, conquered from within through subversion by the Persian King Cyrus (Chapter IV, page 42). History records an endless repetition of such experiences.

Today the long arm of subversion can be organized to reach around the world. It can be aimed to strike through weaker friends or neighbors. Among the many nations with intense internal tensions of race, language, religion, poverty, and hunger, there are endless opportunities for subversion and the organization of violence by trained leaders when the time is ripe. When such campaigns are aimed avowedly at the destruction of the United States, which holds the nuclear umbrella, it becomes pertinent to ask, Where does the defense of the United States and its friends begin?

In an immensely complex world, black and white dividing lines are rare. In a world filled with revolutionary ferment the bases for judgment can change overnight. But human nature and world history make it very clear that this is an enduring dilemma of the human condition. It is likely to remain until the rule of international law can be established and effectively enforced.

In considering the relationship of the great powers to their restless neighbors, it is well to remember that Russia lost many million lives under the surprise attacks of her near neighbor in two world wars and that she has good reason to want secure buffers to protect her own safety. The United States has suffered the same experience in the Pacific, in lesser form, and has equal reason to want a dependable safeguard against the fulminations of a seemingly berserk neighbor. In speaking of this situation at the time of President Kennedy's Administration, Dr. Arthur Schlesinger pointed out that the "domino theory" acquired validity when the neighboring governments staked their security on the power of the United States to back up its pledges to Saigon.

In this morass of intrigues and ambitions, psychology will no doubt play an important part in reaching a solution, and, until the U.N. can achieve the seemingly distant goal of an effective peace force, the good offices of its Secretary-General would appear to be the best hope for maintaining accommodation and understanding among the contending nations. Meanwhile the successes and mistakes of both the Communist and democratic governments, wrestling with the enormous problems of an overfilled and underfed world may hopefully lead to better mutual understanding. Broader economic and social contacts should help to build saner relationships, to break down the trade barriers between nations, and to build new opportunities for the poorer nations to stand on their own feet and survive. Few nations have within their own boundaries the variety of resources they need for self-sufficiency.

This problem of world trade, the exchange of money or goods between nations, has become one of the world's greatest and most baffling problems. It is worldwide, and it is in two parts: In order to buy things it needs from other countries, a nation must produce enough goods above its own needs so that it can exchange them for what it needs from abroad, and in order to trade with a stranger across the ocean who speaks a different language and uses a different currency there must be some accepted standard of value that will apply to both sides of the trade.

No really satisfactory system has yet been devised for this purpose, in spite of intensive international study. Gold is the one standard of value that has been generally agreed on by the nations that engage in international trade, but there is no longer enough gold in the world to take care of the growing needs. The United States dollar has been the nearest approach to gold as the most widely used and trusted currency for trade among nations. This nation has maintained the legal value of the dollar at 35 to the ounce of gold and it supports that value by exchanging dollars for gold in dealing with other governments. Other governments also measure the values of their currencies in gold and agree to maintain these values, which are officially listed by the International Monetary Fund. Some nations have used the pound sterling as the standard of value in addition to the dollar. To support this value the pound must not be allowed to fluctuate more than 2¢ either up or down.

The International Monetary Fund maintains a pool of several billion dollars in gold, and in the currencies of more than 100 nations. Member nations may borrow from this fund up to the limit of their credit, to help in stabilizing their currency values. With each nation the problem in international trade is to earn enough to pay for the things it needs to import. In order to carry on trade among nations, it is important to maintain all currencies at their promised value. This is especially important in the case of the two currencies which are measures of value for the others. These currency values are basically psychological. They depend on the general confidence that these nations have the ability to earn enough in foreign trade to pay for the things they need to buy.

The world saw a dramatic example of this truth in the fall of 1964. England has to buy a large share of her food and other needs from abroad, but she has not produced and sold enough goods to pay for them. Finally, in the midst of a wave of seeming prosperity, the nation drew to the end of her reserves and credit. People began to fear that the pound might be devalued. Many exchanged their pounds for other currencies that might be safer. As the pound became less desirable its value dropped. If it could not be supported at the critical level of $2.78, the pound would have to be devalued. With devaluation would come the possibility of a worldwide upset of international trade.

To check the outflow of money the British government took three steps. It raised taxes to reduce the buying power of its citizens; it raised the Bank of England interest rate to reduce the temptation to borrow and spend, and also to attract money from abroad to get the high interest rate; it also imposed a temporary tariff increase of 15% on some imports —further reducing the temptation to buy abroad. These steps still failed to restore confidence, and the continuing fear led to a near panic and heavy selling of the pound, similar to the runs on banks in the panic of 1932. An agreement was reached with central banks in Canada, the United States, Europe, and Japan to make a total of $3 billion available to Britain as a loan, if needed. This was hailed as the biggest financial rescue operation in history and, together with a loan of $1 billion from the International Monetary Fund, it temporarily restored confidence and gave the British government time to search for remedies for her basic trouble.

This would require that the nation produce enough goods to balance its foreign trade and sell them at a cost to compete with other nations in the markets of the world. Success would depend on such things as wage costs, efficiency of management and equipment, and many other factors that enter into the cost of production. The government imposed controls on wages and prices and other parts of the economy but failed to achieve its objective.

By the autumn of 1967 it had become apparent that the pound could not be supported at its stated price of $2.80. A widespread run on the pound threatened to exhaust the British gold reserve and forced a lowering of the value to $2.40. With this devaluation a machine that was worth £1,000 could be exported and sold for $2,400 instead of $2,800. Everything imported from abroad, on the other hand, would cost correspondingly more. This change in values would increase the ability of the foreigner to buy British goods, while it reduced the ability of the British to buy abroad. This, it was hoped, would help to rebuild Britain's ability to pay her debts, but it raised new problems for her friends abroad, some of whom depended largely for their own income on what they could sell to her.

A number of the smaller nations were forced to devalue their own currencies to meet the emergency. Some felt the need to raise their interest rates to discourage the flow of money seeking a higher return in England. The higher interest, in turn, would lower the ability to build houses and other necessary activities. The repercussions from the British situation would thus send a spreading wave of complications through the entire non-Communist world.

The U.S. dollar, the world's basic currency, has also faced some severe hazards which complicate the effort to build a more orderly and stable world. The nation has consistently been able to export more than it imported, but in recent years it has sent huge sums of money abroad for military and economic assistance, diplomatic relations, and many other purposes. Even tourists traveling abroad have taken out billions of dollars more than are brought into the United States by foreign tourists. Thus the United States has been steadily depleting its stock of gold, as foreign governments, especially France, turn in their surplus dollars to be redeemed in gold. This surplus gold, pouring into other nations, has done much to build their prosperity, and U.S. efforts to check the flow raise some problems for them. With its enormous productive power the nation should have no trouble paying its debt over a period of time, but the steady loss of gold places a clear limit on its ability to assist the developing nations and to meet other responsibilities as a world leader. Another international financial crisis could put the dollar in a very dangerous position if enough people were to lose confidence in it and start a run similar to that on the pound.

One of the great obstacles to orderly world trade and to the ability of nations to achieve a safe trade balance lies in the difference in living standards and productive abilities and in the tariffs and other artificial barriers that are set up to protect them from competition. The great need is to find some way to remove these barriers. The European Economic Community has proved that great benefits can be achieved if the national differences can be worked out, and in the process it has been possible to see some of the obstacles that lie in the way of such a forward-looking program.

Six European nations—Belgium, France, Italy, Luxembourg, the Netherlands, and West Germany—undertook to remove, so far as possible, the tariff barriers between themselves and to establish a common trade and tariff policy in dealing with other nations. As a more distant objective, there was the hope of working toward political unity, if economic unity could first be achieved. Great Britain expressed her interest in joining, but she had special problems in her relationship with her Commonwealth partners. She was buying most of New Zealand's lamb, mutton, and dairy products and a large share of Australia's wheat and meat. If she were to be forced to raise her tariffs to nonmember nations, her membership in the Common Market would be a heavy blow to some of her Commonwealth partners, unless she could get a guarantee that they would be given reasonable access to the market for their exports.

The scope of the Common Market membership potential is tremendous. Starting with more than 174 million people and one of the world's most highly industrialized areas, it might, if successful, look forward to including some of the highly developed surrounding nations in the future, to give it a population around 300,000,000. Even within itself there have been several formidable obstacles to unity, especially in the field of agriculture. For example, France, with its fertile land and good climate for farming, is the Common Market's biggest producer of farm products, and she exports a considerable amount to her neighbors in the Common Market. It is to her interest to keep farm prices low enough to attract buyers and to have external tariffs high enough to discourage imports from nonmember nations. The French government has assisted in various ways toward keeping prices low. Farmers in West Germany, on the other hand, hampered by a cooler climate, higher wages, and less fertile land, have not been able to supply all the needed food; thus, Germany has been forced to import food. It is to her interest both to pay prices high enough to attract imports of food and to keep tariffs low enough to permit them to come in. German food prices in 1963 were about 30% higher than those in France.

Germany had earlier set a tariff of 4.5¢ a pound on the import of frozen poultry, which it bought in large quantity from the United States. But, under Common Market agreement, Germany had to raise this tariff to 13.4¢ against imports from nonmember nations. It was estimated that this rise affected $46 million worth of trade with the U.S. This hurt not only the poultry farmers, but also the producers of grain and expensive equipment which went into their production, as well as the many jobs that were involved. It led the U.S. to raise duties on some French and German products, thereby exerting pressure to find some reasonable compromise.

Through many disagreements and compromises, the pressures of common sense have been working against the forces of national ambitions and historic rivalries, and toward unity and order in Europe. Since the inauguration of the project in 1958 the internal tariffs of the Common Market have been greatly reduced, and the volume of trade between its member nations has increased even more.

Europe is only a small part of the world, and the benefits to the nations of the Common Market clearly indicate the benefits that might come to other nations through the same process. However, the varying problems of other vastly different nations are far more complicated than those for the highly developed nations of Europe. The developing nations of Africa, Asia, and South America, being chiefly in need of help and having less to offer in the way of reciprocal tariff reduction, really present a different problem. In 1964, at the U.N. Conference on Trade and Development, a group of the poorer nations, controlling a majority of votes in the U.N. assembly, agreed among themselves to work for the fulfillment of their special needs.

The products that the underdeveloped nations have to sell are largely agricultural or other primary products, whose prices have been falling or fluctuating on the world markets. On the other hand the products that they must acquire for their development are chiefly manufactured goods whose prices have been rising with the rising costs of production in the industrial countries. This means that the poorer nations have been losing ground in their trade with the others. During the 1950's the underdeveloped nations' share of world trade had dropped from 30% to 20%, and the value of their exports had dropped 26%, while the share of the industrialized West had risen from 60% to 66%, and that of the Communist nations had risen from 8% to 12%. It was estimated that if the trend continued at the same rate, the unfavorable trade balance of $3 billion against the poor nations in 1960 would rise to $20 billion by 1970.

The underdeveloped bloc of nations insisted that, to get on their feet, they needed four basic forms of trade concessions:

1) World agreements to establish market quotas for their exports at prearranged prices. This would allow them to plan their production and expected receipts. 2) A system under which the developed nations would collect a tax on imports from each other and put the proceeds into a special fund to help the poorer nations with their development projects. This would mean, in effect, that the taxpayers in the buying countries would pay a little more for the products of the others. 3) Nonreciprocal tariff cuts, just the opposite of the G.A.T.T. program. The richer countries, in other words, would cut or eliminate the tariffs on imports from the poorer nations without compensating cuts by them in return. 4) Turning the U.N. Conference on Trade and Development into a permanent body with power to review world trade policies.

There is little question that future world stability will require some large-scale and coordinated approach to the building up of the poorer nations, but these four trade proposals run into some rather stubborn facts of life. Britain faced the fact that, depending on imported products for her survival and having the world's largest import trade per capita, her taxpayers would be paying far more than their fair share of the cost of the tax on imports. Her sterling crisis also brought out sharply the fact that, rather than importing goods, she must cut down on her imports and build her export trade—not a good argument for granting special concessions to competitors.

The U.S. would also face serious problems under these proposals. With wage and other costs far above the average for most other nations, an industry such as cotton, that has grown behind a protective tariff, would be very hard hit by a one-sided opening of the tariff door, hurting farmers, jobs, and manufacturers. The same would be true of a number of other industries. The fact was also brought out that agreements to support commodity markets and prices for products that were already overabundant would tend to increase the output and depress the prices still further.

The majority vote of the poor-nation group in the U.N. assembly opens up some serious questions. The United States has carried far more than its proportionate share of the cost of the U.N. operations and yet, in the assembly, the U.S. has just one vote, the same as Malta, Gabon, or Iceland, each with populations not over one two-hundredth that of the U.S.

With all its weaknesses the U.N. is the world's biggest and most far-reaching step in the effort toward international sanity. Basically it offers the opportunity for the nations of the world to learn to know each other, to understand all sides of their common problems, and to exchange ideas, even though this is often done in the form of invective and misrepresentation. It offers a means of educating world opinion and of cooperative effort toward solving international problems. It has shown that it can exert a strong influence for order and peace—if it can be held together and if the more developed nations can be persuaded that it is worth the cost to them who must carry the major part of the cost.

In or out of the U.N., there appear grounds for hope that the Cold War may be liquidating itself. Each of the opposing sides has within itself dangerous internal problems, and each has evolutionary forces that search for change and progress. The crowding populations and complexity of life in the Western nations tend toward socialization of government and the cutting down of personal freedoms. On the other hand, the Communist attempt at changing human nature through cradle-to-grave indoctrination seems to be attempting that change in a direction that does not attract civilized human nature. The two systems tend toward experiences and modifications that could bring them to a common meeting ground some time in the future. Meanwhile the underdeveloped nations gain time to acquire experience, education, and understanding of the world around them, and to seek help from the richer nations in the development of stable populations and self-sustaining economies.

CHAPTER XVI

Population Pressures and the Developing Nations

In Chapter I we saw the deer of the Kaibab Forest multiply beyond the carrying capacity of their range. The resulting pressure on the plants that had fed them not only destroyed much of the ability of the range to support them but resulted in mass starvation which decimated the deer herd. Among the newly developing nations of the world we see human populations that have been following the same course. Medical science has lifted the natural controls that had kept their numbers in balance with the carrying capacity of their land, and they have multiplied to the point where their land can no longer support them in their former way of life.

Without the knowledge or the skills needed to live under the new conditions of their environment, these people face the question: Can they learn to adapt themselves to survive under the conditions imposed by their new environment? The industrialized nations can bring them knowledge and help, but even modern science has still a lot to learn about the requirements for successful agriculture in tropical climates and untried soils. There is the enormous problem of bringing the needed knowledge and equipment to hundreds of millions of illiterate people, as well as the still greater problem of persuading them to control their exploding numbers to keep them within the capacity of the new methods to feed them.

These new nations are becoming a great potential force in the world, searching for cohesion among themselves, searching for education and understanding of the new environment into which they have been thrust. Armed, in many cases, with modern weapons, their numbers and potential strength give them the potential balance of power in the U.N. and great bargaining power in the confrontation between the Communist and Western nations. Their hunger, illiteracy, and inexperience confronts the Western nations with the imperative need for help in attaining order, education, and the stability for self-government.

This need has enlisted huge amounts of help from the industrialized nations, but many of the hungry nations, in spite of all assistance, have actually slipped backward in the ability to feed themselves. Overwhelmed by growing numbers, they were producing less food for each hungry new mouth in 1966 than they were ten years earlier. It appears that, for them, the billions of dollars contributed for food and development may actually have hurt more than they helped. The growing hunger brings social and political instability that threatens to destroy their ability to govern themselves. It is no service to a starving nation to feed two hungry mouths if the process results in four that will curse it for having produced them.

For most of the developing nations the problem is much more urgent than in the United States and Western Europe. Among our neighbors in Latin America there were, in 1966, thirteen nations with growth rates approximately double that of the United States. In mid-1966 these nations had a population that totaled more than 198 million, and it was growing at a rate that would double its numbers in less than 23 years. This means that, if the rate continues, the number will exceed

396 million in 1989, and by the year 2035, when many of today's youth will be mature, it will pass 1½ billion.

No doubt environmental resistance will slow this growth long before these figures are reached, for there seems no possibility that the productive power of the continent can feed such numbers or that the crowding populations can stand the tensions that they will generate. But, short of war or starvation, the process will be long and cruel, and the time for remedy is short.

The Western world has been slow in awakening to the seriousness of this situation which was emphasized by Dr. Raymond Ewell, Vice-President for Research, State University of New York, and former adviser to the government of India. In an address before a division of the American Chemical Society in Chicago, September 1, 1964, he said: "If present trends continue it seems likely that famine will reach serious proportions in India, Pakistan, and China in the early 1970's, followed by Indonesia, Iran, Turkey, Egypt, and several other countries within a few years, and then followed by most of the other countries of Asia, Africa, and Latin America by 1980. Such a famine will be of massive proportions affecting hundreds of millions, possibly even billions of persons. If this happens, as appears very probable, it will be the most colossal catastrophe in history. It will be a completely new situation in the world's history. . . ."

During the ten years ending in 1964, while huge international efforts at relief were going forward, the population of the world increased by more than 500,000,000 people, and, of these, more than 400,000,000 hungry mouths descended on the shoulders of the already hungry underdeveloped nations. All the developed nations of the world already have the ability to control their own growth rates, but with many of the underdeveloped countries no method has yet proved adequate. Even with the knowledge and the materials supplied, the flood of births has continued. Progress is being made, and conditions change, but as late as 1964 Paul and William Paddock, in their book *Hungry Nations,* reported that hospital records in Chile showed that, for every hundred live births in hospitals there were 31 hospitalizations due to induced abortion; for every 100 general admissions into emergency hospitals, 42 were for complications resulting from induced abortions; moreover, 35% to 40% of all pregnancies in Chile resulted in induced abortions. This seems to suggest that there is some psychological block between the availability of birth control methods and the initiative to use them, even though the dangers of an abortion are preferable to the disaster of another child to feed. Testifying before Senator Gruening's Subcommittee on Foreign Aid Expenditures in the fall of 1966, Dr. Alan F. Guttmacher, the noted obstetrician, estimated that about one pregnancy in five in the United States is terminated illegally and that the total of deaths throughout the world from abortion would probably equal the total from cancer or heart disease.

Population control is the essential foundation for progress, but at best it will take time to become effective, and hundreds of millions are already fighting against starvation. Salvation for them means greater food production. To achieve modern agricultural productivity is not just a matter of working harder. For the underdeveloped countries it means a revolution in the nation's way of life. For a largely illiterate people it means acquiring the education, the knowledge, and the equipment for research into the agricultural needs and potentials of the local soils and climate. It means developing crops that are suited to the local environment and learning the best methods of raising them; for crops and methods that are successful in a temperate northern environment may fail in a hot southern climate and different soils. In a land with more debts than credits, it means finding the capital to pay the costs of educating teachers, technicians, and pupils, and for purchasing equipment for research. It means building an economy that can produce or buy the tools and equipment—the pesticides, fertilizer, tractors, oil, gas, and a host of other essentials.

To produce all these things requires factories and know-how. To maintain such factories requires roads, harbors, railroads, and airplanes to bring in raw materials and to carry out the products to consumers. It requires a market, with enough people and money to buy the continuing output of the factory, and it requires knowledge and technical ability to market these products in competition with the richer nations which already have their industries established.

The industrialized nations can give help and money to get such undertakings started, but that is little use unless the recipients have the resources, the education, and the markets to keep them functioning. When one thinks of a developing nation it is natural to think of it as a unit that can think and plan for itself. It would be helpful to keep in mind that many nations are rather artificial combinations of vastly different peoples, religions, languages, and economic interests, and the best of programs can be broken down by internal dissension. Nigeria, for example, has nearly 250 different tribes, almost every one with its own language.

Among the least developed of the newly emerging states in Africa, Malawi (formerly Nyasaland) is fairly representative of the conditions to be met. On gaining its independence in 1964 it had a population of nearly 4 million, most of them small farmers, with an estimated average income of about $60 a year. Until it gained independence it had been exploited for three cash crops—tea, tobacco, and cotton—that had been grown on large plantations owned and managed chiefly by white settlers.

On gaining its independence the nation faced the problem of governing itself without knowledge, experience, or resources. In the entire country there was just one lawyer, one engineer, not a single native stenographer, and no scientists. It had not more than about 400 native citizens who had completed secondary school, and about 50 who had any university education, this having been acquired outside the country. The country had to depend on foreigners to fill about 90% of the high-level jobs that required at least a secondary school education.

The country had an elementary school system in which most of the teachers had no more than an elementary education themselves. Less than half the children of elementary school age attended school, and, out of 33,000 who had started school in 1951, only 620 had completed ten years of school. The country faced the task, not only of educating its children, but also of finding the means of educating teachers before it could even start to run its own affairs.

India, the world's second largest nation, is an example of one that has advanced further than many, but is still far from self-supporting. Her population of about 470 million in 1963 has increased at a rate of more than 10 million a year. This population, representing many different racial origins, languages, and cultural beliefs, is spread out through 570,000 small villages and nearly 2,700 larger towns and cities. To serve these communities she has a very inadequate ground transportation system which totaled, in 1961, only 440,000 miles of surfaced and unsurfaced roads and railroads.

With about 70% of all her workers engaged in agriculture, millions of her farmers had holdings of 2 acres or less, not enough to support a family. Less than half her population was within the most productive ages of 20 to 60. Her huge population had outgrown the capacity of the land to support it under its ancient methods of agriculture, and most of the people were perpetually hungry. Of the millions of young people who would survive the ordeal of permanent malnutrition, a large share would suffer lifelong mental and physical retardation, and, while undernourished, would be perpetually tired and more subject to disease—a poor background for self-help. To provide this huge population with just two ounces apiece of food grain a day would take around 10 million tons a year. To distribute it to the scattered villages over the fragmentary road system would be a monumental undertaking. To create jobs for the four to five million new additions to the labor force each year would require capital investments of about $200 apiece, or roughly a billion dollars.

In the years 1951 to 1961 the nation had increased its food production by 37%, but here it reached a sort of plateau, and in the next three years it made little gain, while its population was increasing by 30 million. Meanwhile, its production of rice per acre was roughly only a third that of Japan and its cotton production per acre, only a fifth that of Egypt.

India has tremendous natural resources—if only they can be properly developed. In 1963 she had about 70 million acres of agricultural land under irrigation, with about 100 million more believed to be irrigable if water sources could be developed from underground supplies and from the abundant unharnessed rivers. But the construction of dams, canals, wells, and machinery to irrigate 100 million acres is a colossal undertaking, and to find the money, the equipment, and the skills, no less a problem. Thus there is the challenge of building the foundation, or substructure, to support the development of these resources.

Besides her farmland, India has 140 million acres of forest, one of the world's largest reserves of high quality iron ore, good supplies of coal, and a variety of other minerals, including petroleum and thorium, a source of atomic energy. There are large reserves of unused waterpower for the generation of electricity. But, to use all these resources, India, with a low rate of literacy, needs to build a foundation of trained scientists, teachers, technicians, and administrators adequate to handle the task.

Huge amounts of money are needed to build this foundation, and planners need to know in advance how much to expect from foreign trade, foreign aid, and private investment. India has been receiving about $1 billion a year in foreign aid from several countries, with about 40% of the total coming from the United States. To achieve a balanced program she needs to know what proportion of all this money can be allocated to each one of the many needs. How much will be required for improved seed, for fertilizer, for machinery, for roads, for engineers, for storage space?

A large part of India's ability to buy needed supplies from

outside depends on her ability to raise and export such "money crops" as tea, cotton, and jute. From 1958 to 1962 the price of tea, one of her key exports, dropped 30%, upsetting plans and nullifying a large share of the help she received through foreign aid. After providing for vital agricultural needs, how much of the remaining funds can be spared for education, for essential power production, and for factories? What kinds of education deserve first priority, and in what proportion?

With all her problems, India has made good advances in her development. From 1951 to 1961 her national income rose from $21 billion (99 billion rupees) to $30 billion. Her industrial output rose by 100%. Her school attendance for children in the age group from 6 to 11 rose from 43% in 1951 to 60% in 1961. The number of students in the higher secondary schools and universities increased nearly two-and-one-half times. The number of engineering and technical colleges rose from 49 to 100, and the enrollment in colleges and institutions teaching engineering, agriculture, and veterinary sciences multiplied fourfold. A beginning was made in the establishment of a nationwide system of health services, with the promotion of family planning as a central feature.

In her race with famine, India has given an especially vivid demonstration of the psychological tensions that are present in different forms in so many of the world's nations and that are sharpened by hunger. With a population speaking more than 170 different languages, the problem of administering the huge country can easily be imagined. The most widely used language is Hindi. In order to simplify the problem the government, in 1965, decreed that Hindi should be the official means of communication. Millions who could not speak Hindi saw this as an obstacle to their chance of getting government employment. The wild rioting, with many deaths that followed, leading to cabinet resignations, emphasized the obstacles that language differences can impose.

Among India's sources of tension, perhaps none is more disrupting than the antagonism between religious faiths. Hatreds between Moslem and Hindu are sharpened by memories of the bloodbath of 1947 when the area was first separated into the nations of India and Pakistan. Nearly a million people are estimated to have died in the disturbances at that time. But there are still left in India nearly fifty million Moslems, living among a sea of Hindus, and ten million Hindus living among the ninety million of other faiths in Moslem Pakistan. In the hungry land of India the Hindu venerates the cow and would rather starve than eat its sacred meat. In November, 1966, when the country was on the verge of famine, a mob of Hindus estimated at 100,000, led by holy men smeared with ashes, rioted in New Delhi to protest against the slaughter of cattle. Such religious antipathies come to a focus in the struggle over predominantly Moslem Kashmir. India had promised to hold a plebiscite to determine Kashmir's eventual allegiance. But, foreseeing the probable result, India has never permitted a vote, and most of Kashmir remains under Indian rule.

Even though the responsible rulers might want to permit a vote, there has been the fear that the resulting tensions might lead to a "holy war" and the breakup of India. Meanwhile the world watched the two nations throwing away their resources in a futile war over Kashmir that threatened the people with starvation worse than before.

In 1962 the Chinese attack on India's northeastern border disrupted the Indian development program, calling for a great diversion of effort and an aggregate increase of 20% in her level of taxation. Communist influence has been strong in some parts of India, notably in Kerala, and the emotion-torn nation has been fertile ground for trained agitators. City after city has been crippled by general strikes, in many cases led by Communists. In Hyderabad, rioters, protesting plans to locate a new government-owned steel mill outside their state, wrecked railway stations, burned railway cars, and cut telephone lines, thus further crippling the power of government to help them. Hunger, despair, ignorance, religious fanaticism, and the mob instinct seem to combine into an almost suicidal sort of frenzy.

In 1965 and 1966 record-breaking droughts brought India face to face with famine. This possible disaster was warded off by millions of tons of grain from the American reserves, thereby reducing these reserves to near the danger point. American grain production can be increased, but India is only one of the many developing nations whose food output has been falling behind their output of hungry mouths and bitter hearts. No amount of food increase can long keep pace with the present increase of people. Gifts of food, money, and education don't build self-sufficiency unless they are part of a well-balanced program, adapted to the individual country's special needs and resources and managed by a reasonably honest and competent government. Effective aid has to be a sort of partnership based on careful study of the needs and planning of the overall program. The willingness of the donor to help must, in the long run, be based on his belief that the recipient is effectively carrying out the agreed program.

Under the conditions that we have just considered, such a partnership must require as much deft understanding of human nature as it does of scientific and economic competence; and above all it requires effective work to control the multiplication of population—far more effective than that which most of the developing nations have yet achieved.

The Western nations have watched with puzzled interest and some hope the upheavals in the Communist world, which seemed to be turning Communist attention inward toward internal problems, and away from the idea of world revolution. But the proponents of the world revolution still have one most effective agent working in their favor. Until the population explosion can be curbed, the revolutionists have only to wait until growing hunger brings the chaos they are waiting for. They are a most important part of the human environment, and it is well to remember that their method of attack is subtle and disguised. They have yet to prove that their form of government is any more successful or acceptable to its citizens than the more democratic forms, with all their faults. From the Western point of view they offer a most compelling reason for speed and success in bringing stability to the nations that need it. For all the repulsive aspects and much-publicized failures of Communism, both Russia and China achieved results, against almost impossible conditions, that would have been impossible under more cumbersome democratic forms of government. The evolution of civilization appears to have reached a crossroad where giant forces are contending for the driver's seat, to determine whether man shall develop into a community of human termites, or whether he can find the wisdom to govern his relations with his fellows in peace and disciplined freedom. The decision on that point would appear to depend on whether he will face up to the implications of human multiplication in time to bring it under control before he breeds himself into the termite nest where dictatorship need only wait for his arrival. It appears to be within the developing nations that the decisive action must be carried out. It is especially worth remembering that Japan has showed the world that it can be done. Within the short space of ten years, from 1947 to 1957 she cut her birth rate in half.

CHAPTER XVII

The Search for Civilization

In this book we have searched for the implications of civilization and have seen some of the conflicts that arise in the confrontation between civilization and human nature. At bottom it boils down to a story of life and the laws that govern it. At the beginning of the book we saw these laws at work in the natural community of plants and animals. In the course of the book we have seen them at work in the human community. These laws do not appear very obvious in the day-to-day conduct of life. Working slowly, through unseen reactions, they cause changes in the environment that affect the course of future events. The consummation of these chain reactions is often so slow that their significance is easily missed, but they may affect all life within their environment.

In the first chapter we saw a simple example of such a chain reaction. In the growing forest the mere deepening of the shadows on the forest floor was enough to eliminate both the pioneer species of trees that had built the forest and the community of living things that had depended on the environment that the trees established. This change was brought about not by any damage to the trees themselves but by the shadows which deprived the growing seedlings of the life-giving sunlight. Their place was taken by the seedlings of other species that could thrive in the shade. These, in turn, grew up to build a deeper shade and so eliminated their own species to make way for others.

Thus the environment imposes the conditions that dominate life within it. Chief among these conditions is the law which forbids the crowding of life beyond the carrying capacity of the environment. We saw how nature provides the controls to enforce this law. For this purpose she uses predators, ranging from the tiger to the invisible bacterium. We saw how vertebrate creatures, including man, are equipped with instincts which guide them automatically to conform with this and other requirements of natural law. These instincts include the drives for domination, for defense of home territory, and for aggression. Man, with the development of his brain, has

141

forced himself into a dilemma. He has changed his environment so drastically that many of his ancient instincts, which served him so well in the past, are no longer adapted to serve him in the new environment that he has built. His aggressiveness and his group antagonisms, among others, now threaten his very existence.

It is sometimes said that man has progressed to the point where he is largely independent of his environment. To say this is to ignore our urban gigantism and decay, our spreading juvenile delinquency and crime, the psychological crippling of huge slum populations, the pollution of air and water, the wholesale malnutrition of half the world's population, and the worldwide revolutionary ferment which challenges man's ability to govern himself and to prepare future generations for self-government. These are all man-made parts of today's unnatural human environment. They come as chain reactions from past events, and they have a direct bearing on the human future. With all his intelligence, man has proved himself to be just as subject to the basic laws of ecology as are his fellow animals.

The condition of our major domestic problems leaves room for optimism that they can be solved. No doubt our growing productivity can supply our physical needs, and experience can lead to more efficient management of our human relations. There is still the unanswered question of how to produce a citizenship that is really qualified for self-government under today's conditions and that can live life at a higher level than a colony of ants. In the development of such citizens, how is society to replace the standards, the motivations, the conditioning that were formerly supplied by home, church, school, community, and tradition? How is it to provide the incentives to initiative that were formerly supplied by the open frontiers of opportunity for all? What chain reactions of motivation will spread through the generations of a society wherein the basic needs of all are taken care of by a benign government? History cannot provide very reassuring answers. New knowledge and new methods must find new answers for today.

Chief among the "shadows" in today's environment is the world explosion of population. This is one of the chain reactions set in motion by the explosion of scientific knowledge, especially by the series of medical discoveries which resulted, by the mid-twentieth century, in the conquest of some of man's oldest and deadliest diseases. The joy in this accomplishment soon turned to dismay, for these diseases were nature's controls to which the human birth rate had become adjusted. Their removal broke the balance between incoming and outgoing life on the earth. The subsequent rise in population numbers began to overwhelm the food supply.

Science answered the population rise with increased food production. But this increase failed to keep pace with the population in many areas, so that the share of food for each hungry mouth continued to shrink. We know that science has the means to control population growth and that the industrial nations are bringing their own growth rates under control. But these nations are no longer independent of their fellow members of the world community. It has become very clear that world stability is going to depend on the development of a self-sustaining world community. That consummation will depend on the ability of the hungry countries to control and feed their own populations, with essential help from the richer nations toward getting on their feet. That effort turns into a life-and-death race between progress and population.

In some of the hungriest and fastest-growing nations, this race turns into an obstacle race where ignorance and illiteracy, together with traditional and religious taboos, pose psychological problems that are as difficult as the physical ones. In 1966 while India was accepting millions of tons of food from the United States to ward off famine among its multiplying people, the Indian press, including the conservative *Times of India*, viciously attacked the U.S. for advocating birth control after having recently opposed it at home. Hungry mobs in the state of Kerala derailed trains and destroyed equipment that could have been used to bring them food. Other mobs rioted and killed to protest the use of surplus sacred cows for food. Even in the United Nations there has been great reluctance to take an affirmative action to control this world affliction. In offering needed help to hungry nations, those who have the help to give have sometimes been dismayed to find that the offer has brought a suspicion of condescension which can quickly turn gratitude into dislike and opposition.

Today the world is concerned with the problems of producing enough food and controlling enough multiplication to ward off famine. If that can be achieved, the problem does not stop there. All nations will still be closely concerned with maintaining a balance between world population and world carrying capacity. There will be more need than ever before for world agreement on the managing of international relationships. With world population still increasing between 50 and 60 million each year, the problem of overcrowding will certainly grow worse before it can be controlled. Among other questions will be the measurement of world carrying capacity. Is it the number of people who can be supported above the level of starvation, the number who can be contented enough to maintain a stable government, the number who can be fed without help from outside? Should some nations even aspire to the number which will allow the best opportunity for a full, developed life to all?

The carrying capacity of a nation depends, as we have seen, on the status of its relations with other nations. England, for example, is filled beyond the capacity of its home land to produce the necessary food. But the environment of England reaches across the world. As long as she can produce things that other people will buy in exchange for food, she can still be self-supporting. But some of the poorer nations are not so fortunate. We have seen that some of them feel that, in order to survive, they must have special trade concessions from the industrialized nations to create markets for their products. The ability of other nations, including England, to make such concessions, is not always commensurate with the needs. The carrying capacity of India and many other nations is a circular affair. Rioting mobs, burdensome armies, fear of neighbors, and internal subversion all serve to reduce native carrying capacity and to nullify the aid efforts of their friends.

Humanity is crossing the threshold into a new world. To conquer the problems of food supply and population control will call for the coordinated efforts of every nation. Today such efforts are crippled by national rivalries, suspicions, and ideologies. The effort will require not just food production and education. It will require the building within the hungry nations of the substructure that can make succesful production possible. Most important of all, it will require the building within man of the necessary motivations.

History records the incessant conflict between man's instinctive savagery and his acquired civilizing motivations. We saw how, even in early Mesopotamia, the city gods were central features of civilization—builders of motivation for order, discipline, and unity in the cities, and, when wisely used, a potential binding force between cities. Later the great world religions, despite their many weaknesses, contributed enormously to human progress. We have seen how every culture, through family, precept, and tradition, conditions its members with their characteristic motivations for order and social unity. Today, under the pressures of an unnatural environment, the old sources of civilized motivations are weakening. Like the shadows on the forest floor, this change strikes at the coming generations, determining what kind of creature the future man will be.

What can we foretell for the future? Professor Lewis Mumford has pointed out that man faces two alternative kinds of future—first there is the probable future, foreshadowed by the trends of history and the development of human institutions. This is not a very pleasing prospect. Then, there is another kind of future, made possible by the potentials within man.

Today we know that man has new potentials for progress which he never had before. He has growing knowledge and fantastic new equipment for its use. He has a growing understanding of himself and the forces that govern him. He has a growing understanding of the natural resources on which all life depends. Through his use of science, man has burdened himself with the population explosion and the hydrogen bomb. But science, in offering him new understanding and the means to use it, offers him also the instruments for the solution of his dilemma.

Civilization has persisted through ages of savagery and genocide, famine and pestilence, misery and revolution. Now, with newer understanding of himself, man has a new opportunity to achieve the kind of civilization that he desires.

BIBLIOGRAPHY

MAN IN THE WEB OF LIFE

Chapters 1 and 2

Allee, Emerson, Park, Park, Schmidt. *Principles of Animal Ecology*, W. B. Saunders Co., Philadelphia, 1951.
Robert Ardrey. *African Genesis*. Atheneum, New York, 1961.
────── *The Territorial Imperative*. Atheneum, New York, 1966.
Konrad Lorenz. *On Aggression*. Harcourt Brace and World, New York, 1966.

Chapter 3

Ernst Mayr. *Animal Species and Evolution*. Harvard University Press, Cambridge, 1963.
Carleton S. Coon. *The Origin of Races*. Knopf, New York, 1962.

Chapter 4

James G. Macqueen. *Babylon*. Praeger, New York, 1965.
James Mellaart. *Earliest Civilizations of the Near East*. McGraw-Hill, New York, 1965.
Lewis Mumford. *The City in History*. Harcourt Brace and World, New York, 1961.
────── address before conference on *Future Environments of North America*, Doubleday, New York, 1965.
Eustace D. Phillips. *The Royal Hordes*. McGraw-Hill, New York, 1965.
Paul B. Sears. *Deserts on the March*. University of Oklahoma Press, Norman, Oklahoma, 1935.
John H. Storer. *The Web of Life*. Signet, New York, 1956.

Chapter 5

Mumford. (See Chapter 4.)
Eugene R. Black. "Population Increase and Economic Development," in *Our Crowded Planet*. Fairfield Osborn, ed., Doubleday, New York, 1962.
M. C. Chagla. "India's Dilemma," in *Our Crowded Planet, op. cit.*
Periodicals
William I. Langer. "The Black Death," *Scientific American*. CCX, February 1964, pp. 114-118.

Chapter 6

Harrison Brown. *The Challenge of Man's Future.* Viking, New York, 1954.

Lester R. Brown. *Man, Land and Food.* Foreign Agricultural Economic Report #11, 1963, U.S. Department of Agriculture.

John B. Calhoun. *A Comparative Study of the Social Behavior of Two Inbred Strains of House Mice.* National Institute of Mental Health, Bethesda, Md. A reprint from *Ecological Monographs* 26, January 1956, pp. 81-103.

Rachel Carson. *Silent Spring.* Houghton Mifflin, Boston, 1962.

Chikao Honda. "Japan's Solution," in *Our Crowded Planet.* (See Chapter 5.)

Frederick Osborn. "Overpopulation and Genetic Selection," in *Our Crowded Planet.* (See Chapter 5.)

Philip M. Hauser. *Population Perspectives.* Rutgers University Press, Rutgers, New Jersey, 1960, p. 71.

Periodicals

"The Story of Mauritius," *Population Bulletin.* XVIII, #5, August 1962.

"Needed: A Population Policy for the World," *Population Bulletin.* XXII, #2, May 1965.

World Population Data Sheet. Population Reference Bureau, December 1965 and 1968.

Alan Gregg. "A Medical Aspect of the Population Problem," *Science.* XXI, #3150, 1955, p. 682.

"The Senate Looks at Population," *Population Bulletin.* XXII, #5, December 1966, p. 119.

Chapter 7

Periodicals

Nevin S. Scrimshaw. "Food," *Scientific American,* CCIX. #3, September, 1963, p. 73.

Lewis S. Anderson. "The Mushroom Crowd," *Journal of the Canadian Medical Association.* XCIV, December 5, 1964.

G. E. Smith and William A. Albrecht. "Feed Efficiency in Terms of Biological Assays of Soil Treatment," *Proceedings of the Soil Science Society of America.* VII, 1942.

Chapter 8

Paul de Bach, ed. *Biological Control of Insect Pests.* Reinhold, New York, 1964.

Allen V. Kneese. "The Economics of Regional Water Quality Management," Report on Study for 'Resources for the Future', contained in its Annual Report, 1963.

"Climate and Man." *U.S. Department of Agriculture Yearbook,* 1941, p. 685.

Periodicals

Raymond L. Nace. "Water of the World," *Natural History Magazine*. LXXIII, September 1964.

George H. Davis. "Management of Water in Arid Lands," *Natural History Magazine*. New York, LXXIII, September 1964.

Roger Revelle. "Water," *Scientific American*. CCIX, #3, September 1963, p. 93.

A. J. Haagen Smit. "The Control of Air Pollution," *Scientific American*. CCX, #1, January 1964, pp. 24–28.

Abel Wolman. "The Metabolism of Cities," *Scientific American*. CCXIII, #3, September 1965, pp. 178–183.

Rachel Carson. "Rachel Carson Testifies," *Massachusetts Audubon Magazine*. Lincoln, XLVIII, Winter 1963.

Clarence Cottam. "Chemical Pesticides, a National Problem," an abstract prepared for National Wildlife Federation, Washington, 1959.

Conservation Newsletter. National Wildlife Federation, Washington, June 15 and October 15, 1964.

James B. De Witt. "Chronic Toxicity to Quail and Pheasants of Some Chlorinated Insecticides," *Agricultural and Food Chemistry*. IV, #10, October 1956, p. 863.

Newspapers

"Biologists Wary on Insect Control," *New York Times*, July 17, 1964, p. 29.

"Omaha to Limit Wastes in River," *New York Times*, April 3, 1966, p. 30.

Report of Committee on Waste Management and Control, Dr. A. Spilhaus, Chairman, National Academy of Sciences, *New York Times*, April 3, 1966.

Chapter 9

Manpower Report of the President of the United States, March 1964, pp. xii, xiii, 27, 34, 105, 151, 160.

Periodicals

"Why American Companies Are Going Abroad," interview of Ray R. Eppert, President of the Burroughs Corporation in *U.S. News and World Report*, LVI, #6, February 10, 1964.

"Picture of a Mayor in Deep Trouble," *U.S. News and World Report*. LX, #3, January 17, 1966.

Newspapers

A. H. Raskin. "Approach to Automation, the Kaiser Plan," *The New York Times Magazine*, November 3, 1963.

Vartanig V. Vartan. "Fourteen Concerns Considering Moving," *The New York Times*, February 17, 1967, p. 40.

Chapter 10

Report of the Council of Economic Advisers, January 1964, Tables C-17, C-52 and C-57.

U.S. Statistical Abstracts. (Government Printing Office, Washington, 1963), Table 468.

Periodicals
"Impact of the Tax Cut," *Newsweek*. October 21, 1963, p. 83.
"Trend of American Business," *U.S. News and World Report*. LVI, #5, February 3, 1964, p. 87.
"Is Private Debt Too Big?" *U.S. News and World Report*. LVI, #7, February 17, 1964, p. 50.

Chapter 11

Periodicals
"Why New York City Is Deeper in Trouble," *U.S. News and World Report*. LVIII, #6, February 8, 1965, p. 40.

Chapter 12

Bernard Berelson and Gary A. Steiner. *Human Behavior*. Harcourt Brace and World, New York, 1964, pp. 64-67, 134, 217.
J. McV. Hunt. *Intelligence and Experience*. Ronald, New York, 1961, pp. 18, 61, 62.
Professor and Mrs. Sheldon Glueck. *Unravelling Juvenile Delinquency*. Harvard University Press, Cambridge, 1950.
Harrison W. Salisbury. *The Shook-up Generation*. Harper, New York, 1958.
Charles E. Silberman. *Crisis in Black and White*. Random House, New York, 1964.
U. S. Statistical Abstracts. (1963), Table 844.

Periodicals
Judge Robert Gardner. "A Judge Tells How to Deal With Underage Hoods." *U.S. News and World Report*. LV, #9, August 26, 1963, p. 44.
"Can We Make Human Beings More Intelligent?" J. McV. Hunt, interviewed by John Kord Lagerman, *Reader's Digest*, May 1966, p. 77.
"Animal Research Proves Brain Expands if Used." *Science News*. LXXIX, #14, April 2, 1966, p. 227.
O. W. Wilson. Special Supplement on Crime. *Harper's Magazine*. CCXXVIII, #1364, April 1964, p. 141.

Chapter 13

Edward T. Hall. *The Hidden Dimension*. Doubleday, New York, 1966, p. 156.
"Report to the President and Congress," Outdoor Recreation Resources Review Commission, Washington, 1962, p. 32.

Chapter 14

James B. Conant. *Slums and Suburbs*. McGraw-Hill, New York, 1961, p. 13.
Max Farrand. *The Records of the Federal Convention of 1778*. Yale University Press, New Haven, 1911.

Robert M. MacIver. *The Web of Government*. Macmillan, New York, 1947, pp. 197, 204.

Ernst Mayr. (See Chapter 3), p. 646.

C. Northcote Parkinson. *The Evolution of Political Thought*. University of London Press, London, 1958, pp. 8, 310–314.

William Vogt. *People*. William Sloane Associates, New York, 1960, p. 78.

U. S. Statistical Abstracts. (1963), p. 56.

Periodicals

"The Senate Looks at Population," *Population Bulletin*. XXII, #5, December, 1966.

"Latest Moves Against Crime in the Streets," *U.S. News and World Report*. LX, #15, March 8, 1965, p. 41.

Chapter 15

Arthur M. Schlesinger, Jr. *A Thousand Days*. Houghton Mifflin, Boston, 1965, p. 538.

Periodicals

"The Common Market," *Population Bulletin*. XVIII, #4, July, 1962, pp. 66-89.

Chapter 16

Paul and William Paddock. *Hungry Nations*. Little Brown, Boston, 1964, pp. 96–97.

Periodicals

Frederick Harbison. "Education for Development," *Scientific American*. CCIX, #3, September 1963, p. 140.

Pitambar Pant. "The Development of India," *Scientific American*. CCIX, #3, September 1963, pp. 189, 192, 200, 202, 205.

Nevin S. Scrimshaw, "Food," *Scientific American*. CCIX, #3, September 1963, p. 73.

Raymond Ewell, as quoted in "World Food Crisis," *Population Bulletin*. XX, #8, December 1964, p. 205.

World Population Data Sheet, Population Reference Bureau, December 1966.

Wolfgang F. Stolper. "The Development of Nigeria," *Scientific American*. CCIX, #3, September 1963, p. 169.

Newspaper

Kushwant Singh. "Why Hindu and Moslem Speak Hate," *The New York Times Magazine,* September 19, 1965, p. 21.

Edwin S. Mason. "The Planning of Development," *Scientific American*. CCIX, #3, September 1963, pp. 240, 243.

Chapter 17

Periodical

Lloyd V. Berkner, address at Colorado College (March 8, 1966) as reported in *Population Bulletin*, XXII, #4, November 1966, p. 92.

Index

Abortions: illegal in U.S., 57, 118, 135; legalizing of, in Japan, 58

Adaptation, law of, in natural community, 18-21

African Genesis (Ardrey), 26

Aggressive destruction against members of same species, 27-28

Aid to Dependent Children, and illegitimate births, 117-18

Air pollution, 15, 70-71, 76, 97, 111

Alakaluf Indians of Tierra del Fuego, development of high basal metabolism of, 32

Albatross and U.S. Navy, contest between, for territorial rights on Midway Island, 23-24

Albert Einstein College of Medicine, 102

Alexander the Great, 42

American Motors Company, progress-sharing plan of, 85

Amino acids, and synthesizing of vegetable proteins, 64

Animal breeding, and development of improvements in breeds, 66, 67

Animal community: biological laws, and survival in, 21-22; automatic self-government of, regulating relations to each other and to their environment, 22; and inherited instincts, 22, 23-28; man's evolution from, 29

Animal products, as source of amino acids, 64

Antiseptics, increasing use of, 46

Ape: man not descended from any living species of, 29; evolution, and pinpointing dividing line between man and, 30; development of physical characteristics in evolution from ape to human, 32

Arable land: of world, decrease in available area of, 53, 69; percentage of world area classified as, 61; factors determining kinds and amounts of foods produced in regions of, 62; variation and

distribution of, among countries, 62, 69; *see also* Productive land

Ardrey, Robert, 23, 24, 26, 29

Australopithecine ape-men, fossils of, 31

Automation, 82, 91

Automobiles, and air pollution, 70, 97

Baboon, and evolutionary background of territoriality and group organization, 25-27

Babylonian empire, 39-42, 125

Bacteria: nature's control of growth of, 16-17, 51; role of, in development of forest, 20; and human health problems, 46

Balance between death rate and birth rate: maintenance of, in baboon community, 26; among humans prior to 19th century, 46; effect of scientific discoveries for control of disease, 47, 142-43; requirement for, imposed by new conditions in today's environment, 119

Bald eagle, and pesticide-infected fish, 56

Beauty in environment, 112-13

"Behavioral sink" resulting from crowding, 110

Berelson, Bernard, 102

Beyond the Melting Pot (Glazier and Moynihan), 108

Biological laws: and environment, 15-21; and survival in the animal world, 21-22; and survival of human life, 76

Birds: and role of song in struggle for survival, 22; nesting of, and carrying capacity of environment, 22-23; and pesticides in earthworms, 55-56, 75

Birth control: as world's best hope for controlling population growth, 57; in U.S., 57-58; and industrial nations, 58; and underdeveloped hungry nations,

151